Math Diagnosis and Intervention System 2.0

BOOKLET J: PROBLEM SOLVING, GRADES 4–6

Teacher's Pages

Intervention Lessons

PEARSON

Glenview, Illinois • Boston, Massachusetts • Chandler, Arizona • Hoboken, New Jersey

PEARSON

ISBN-13: 978-0-328-84896-6
ISBN-10: 0-328-84896-4

3 16

CONTENTS

Booklet **J**

PROBLEM SOLVING
GRADES 4–6

Name ____________

Analyze Given Information

Intervention Lesson J1

Sally's painting is 14 inches long and 12 inches wide. Julie's painting is 16 inches long. How much longer is Julie's painting then Sally's painting?

Solve by answering 1 to 7.

Answer 1 to 4 to **understand** the problem.

1. What do you know from reading the problem?
   Sally's painting is 14 inches long.
   Sally's painting is 12 inches wide.
   Julie's painting is 16 inches long.
2. What do you need to find?
   How much longer is Julie's painting than Sally's painting?
3. Do you have all the information you need to solve the problem? yes
4. What information is not needed to solve the problem?
   The width of Sally's painting is not needed.

Answer 5 and 6 to **plan and solve** the problem.

5. How can you solve the problem? Find 16 minus 14.
6. Solve. How much longer is Julie's painting than Sally's painting? 2 inches

Answer 7 to **look back** at how you solved the problem.

7. Is your answer reasonable? yes

 J1 (student p. 1) MDIS 2.0

Name ____________

Analyze Given Information (continued)

Intervention Lesson J1

How much wider is Sally's painting than Julie's?

Find out by answering 8 and 9.

8. Do you have all the information you need to solve the problem? no
9. What do you need to know in order to solve the problem?
   The width of Julie's painting is needed.

   So, there is not enough information to solve the problem.

Write the extra or missing information. Solve the problem if enough information is given.

10. Jason bought a red sweater and a black sweater. His change was $5. How much did Jason pay for both sweaters?
    Missing information: You need the price of the sweaters.

Write the extra or missing information. Solve the problem if enough information is given.

Use the graph for Exercises 11 and 12.

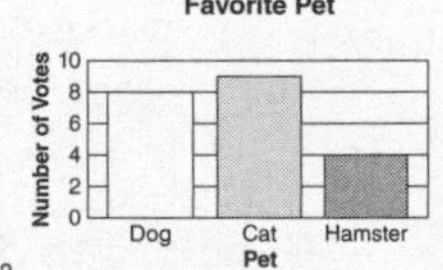

11. Turtles received 4 fewer votes than cats and 2 more votes than rabbits. How many votes did turtles receive?
    2 more votes than rabbits is extra information; 5 votes
12. How many more students voted for dogs than horses?
    Missing information: Horses are not pictured in the graph.
13. **Reasoning** Kim's painting is 12 inches long. Will it fit in a frame that has a length of 12 inches and a width of 8 inches? Explain.
    There is not enough information. The width of Kim's painting is missing.

 J1 (student p. 2) MDIS 2.0

Objective Students will analyze given information.
Vocabulary Analyze

1 Conceptual Development
Use with Exercises 1–9.

In this lesson you will learn to analyze given information.

When students solve real-world problems, they must analyze the given information. Read the problem aloud with students. *What do you know about Sally's painting?* Its length and its width *What do you know about Julie's painting?* Its length *What are you asked to find?* How much longer Julie's painting is than Sally's painting Explain that sometimes there is extra information given that you do not need to answer the question. *What information is given that you do not need?* The width of Sally's painting Have students complete Exercises 1–7. *Why can you not find how much wider Sally's painting is than Julie's?* We do not know how wide Julie's painting is. Explain that sometimes there is not enough information in the problem to answer the question. Have students complete Exercises 8–9.

2 Practice Use with Exercises 10–13.

Tell students that when they are analyzing problems, they can read the question first. Then they will know what information to look for in the problem.

Error Intervention If students have difficulty analyzing problems, have them highlight the information they need to use to solve the problem.

If You Have More Time Have students make up the missing information for any problem that could not be solved. Then have them solve the problem.

3 Assessment

In this lesson students learned to analyze given information. Use the **Quick Check** problem to assess students' understanding.

Quick Check Formative Assessment

Write the extra or missing information and solve the problem if enough information is given: Carly received a score of 95 on her math quiz. James earned a 90, and Tatum earned a 100. How many more points did Tatum earn than Carly? Extra information: "James earned a 90"; 5 points

Name ______________________

Two-Step Problems

Intervention Lesson **J2**

Max earns $9 for every hour he rakes leaves. It took him 2 hours to rake the leaves in his yard. How much money did he earn raking leaves? If he already had $26, how much does he have now?

Solve by answering 1 to 7.

Answer 1 and 2 to **understand** the problem.

1. What do you know from reading the problem?

   Max earns __$9__ for every hour he rakes leaves.

   He raked leaves for __2__ hours.

   He already had __$26__.

2. What do you need to find?
   How much money did Max earn raking leaves?
   How much money did Max have after he raked the leaves?

The problem has two questions. Answer the first one. Then, answer the second one.

Answer 3 to 6 to **plan and solve** the problem.

3. How can you answer the first question? __Multiply 2 times 9.__

4. Solve. How much did Max earn raking leaves? __$18__

5. How can you answer the second question? __Add $26 and $18.__

6. Solve. How much money did Max have after raking leaves? __$44__

Name ______________________

Two-Step Problems (continued)

Intervention Lesson **J2**

Answer 7 to **check** your solution.

7. **Reasoning** Use an estimate to explain why your answer to how much money Max has now is reasonable.
   Max earned about $20 raking leaves and he had about $30. $20 + $30 = $50. Since $44 is close to $50, $44 is reasonable.

Solve each problem. Answer both questions.

8. Ms. Olivia brought 7 bunches of bananas to the school picnic. Each bunch had 5 bananas. She also brought 27 apples.

   How many bananas did she bring? __35__ bananas

   How many more bananas than apples did Ms. Olivia bring? __8__ more

9. There are 3 children and 2 adults in Zac's family. Each person in the family donated $5 to charity.

   How many people are in Zac's family? __5__ people

   How much money did Zac's family donate to charity? __$25__

10. Monique read 45 pages on Saturday and 39 pages on Sunday. Her book has 113 pages.

    How many pages did Monique read? __84__ pages

    How many more pages does she need to read to finish her book? __29__ pages

11. Tandy bought 4 boxes of cat treats. Each box contains 2 packages. It takes 5 days to use each package of cat treats.

    How many packages of cat treats did Tandy buy? __8__ packages

    How many days worth of cat treats did Tandy buy? __40__ days

Objective Students will solve two-step problems.
Vocabulary Two-step problem

1 Conceptual Development

Use with Exercises 1–7.

In this lesson you will learn to solve two-step problems.

Read the problem aloud with students. Explain that this is a two-step problem because there are two questions that have to be answered to solve it. *What do you know after analyzing the problem?* How much Max is paid per hour, how long he works, and how much money he had before raking leaves *What do you want to know?* How much money he earned raking leaves and how much he has now *Was there any extra or missing information?* No Have students complete Exercises 1–2. *What operation will you use to find how much money he made?* Multiplication *What operation will you use to find how much money he has now?* Addition Have students complete Exercises 3–7.

2 Practice Use with Exercises 8–11.

Talk about how, for a two-step problem, the first question must be answered before the second one can be answered.

Error Intervention If students have difficulty solving two-step problems, have them circle the information they need to answer the first question, solve it, and then highlight the information they need to answer the second question.

If You Have More Time Have students write their own two-step problem and present a solution to it.

3 Assessment

In this lesson students learned to solve two-step problems. Use the **Quick Check** problem to assess students' understanding.

Quick Check 

Solve the problem and answer both questions: Barry has 4 pets. His sister has 2 pets. Kevin has 5 pets. How many pets does Barry's family have? How many more pets than Kevin does Barry's family have? 6; 1

Name ____________

Multi-Step Problems

Intervention Lesson J3

At the sports store, Hannah bought 2 baseballs, and Jim bought 3 baseballs. The baseballs cost $6 each. How much did they spend?

Solve by answering 1 to 8.

Answer 1 and 2 to **understand** the problem.

1. What do you know from reading the problem?

   Hannah bought __2 baseballs__.

   Jim bought __3 baseballs__.

   The baseballs cost __$6__ each.

2. What do you need to find?

   How much did Hannah and Jim spend on the baseballs?

Answer 3 to 7 to **plan and solve** the problem.

3. How can you find how much Hannah and Jim spent?

   Multiply the number of baseballs they bought by $6.

4. Does the problem tell you how many baseballs Hannah and Jim bought altogether? __no__

5. Do you have enough information to find out how many baseballs Hannah and Jim bought altogether? __yes__

"How many baseballs did Hannah and Jim buy altogether?" is the **hidden question** in the problem. You need to answer the hidden question before you can solve the problem.

6. How many baseballs did Hannah and Jim buy altogether? __5__

 J3 (student p. 1) MDIS 2.0

Name ____________

Multi-Step Problems (continued)

Intervention Lesson J3

7. How much money did Hannah and Jim spend on the baseballs? __$30__

Answer 8 to **look back and check** your solution to the problem.

8. Did you answer the right question? __yes__

Write and answer the hidden question. Then solve the problem.

9. Henry had 571 baseball cards. He sold 395 of them. He then bought 275 new baseball cards. How many cards does he have now?

   How many baseball cards did Henry have left after he sold 395 of them? 176 cards; 451 cards

Use the graph to answer Exercises 10 and 11.

Favorite Snack	
Fruit	☺ ☺ ☺
Sandwiches	☺ ☺
Cheese	☺
Pretzels	☺ ☺ ☺ ☺

Each ☺ = 3 votes.

10. How many students voted for fruit or cheese?

    How many smiley faces are there for fruit and cheese? 4 smiley faces; 12 students

11. How many more students voted for pretzels than voted for sandwiches?

    How many more smiley faces are there for pretzels than for sandwiches? 2 smiley faces; 6 students

12. It costs $3 to rent a DVD. Sue rented 4 DVDs and Fran rented 3 DVDs. How much did they pay in all?

    How many DVDs did they rent in all? 7 DVDs; $21

13. **Reasoning** Describe another way to find how much Sue and Fran paid in all for the DVDs in Exercise 12.

    Check that students use a different approach than used in Exercise 12. Sample answer: Find how much each spent and then add: $4 \times \$3 = \$12$, $3 \times \$3 = \$9$, and $\$12 + \$9 = \$21$.

 J3 (student p. 2) MDIS 2.0

Objective Students will solve multi-step problems.
Vocabulary Multi-step problem, hidden question

1 Conceptual Development

Use with Exercises 1–8.

In this lesson you will learn to solve multi-step problems.

Read the problem aloud with students. Explain that this is a multi-step problem because there is more than one step required to answer the question. *What do you know after analyzing the problem?* How many baseballs each person bought and the cost of each baseball *What do you want to know?* How much Hannah and Jim spent *Was there any extra or missing information?* No Have students complete Exercises 1–2. *What do you have to find first?* The total number of baseballs they bought Explain that this is the hidden question for this problem. *What operation will you use to answer the hidden question?* Addition Have students complete Exercises 3–6. *What operation will you use to find how much money they spent?* Multiplication Remind students to look back and check their answers. Have students complete Exercises 7–8.

2 Practice Use with Exercises 9–13.

Write the word *multi-step* on the board. Circle the prefix *multi-*. Explain that this prefix means "many or much." In this case, there are many steps that must be taken to solve the problem.

Error Intervention If students have difficulty solving multi-step problems, help them analyze what they need to know to answer the question and whether they have that information or how they will find it.

If You Have More Time Have students describe their thinking and how they determine what the hidden question is.

3 Assessment

In this lesson students learned to solve multi-step problems. Use the **Quick Check** problem to assess students' understanding.

Quick Check 

Find and answer the hidden question and then solve the problem: Kyle bought 4 books. Karen bought 5 books. Each book costs $8. How much did they spend in all? "How many books did they buy altogether?"; 9; $72

Name ______________________

Two-Step Problems

Intervention Lesson J4

Susan has 2 collections of stickers. She has 36 stickers in one collection and 25 stickers in the other collection. If she gives a friend 6 stickers from the first collection, how many stickers in all does she have left?

Solve by answering 1 and 2 to **understand** the problem.

1. What do you know from reading the problem?

   Susan has __2__ collections of stickers.

   One collection has __36__ stickers.

   The other collection has __25__ stickers.

   Susan gives __6__ stickers to a friend.

2. What do you need to find?
   How many stickers Susan has left after she gives 6 stickers to her friend?

Answer 3 and 4 to **plan and solve** the problem.

This problem has a hidden question. You must solve the hidden question before you can solve the problem.

3. What is the hidden question?
   How many stickers does Susan have in both sticker collections?

   Write and solve a number sentence to answer the Hidden Question.

   __36__ + __25__ = __61__

Answer to the Hidden Question: __61__ stickers

4. How many stickers are left after Susan gives 6 stickers to a friend? Write and solve a second number sentence.

   __61__ − __6__ = __55__

   __55__ stickers

 J4 (student p. 1) MDIS 2.0

Name ______________________

Two-Step Problems (continued)

Intervention Lesson J4

Answer 5 to **look back** at how you solved the problem.

5. **Reasoning** Did you answer the right questions? Explain.
   Check student's work. Accept all reasonable responses.

Solve each of the following problems. Remember to look for and write a hidden question that needs to be solved first.

6. Sally ordered 6 packages of pens and 5 packages of pencils for the school supply store. Each package contains 10 pens or pencils. How many pens and pencils did she buy in all?

   Hidden Question: How many packages of pens and pencils did she buy in all?

   Answer to the Hidden Question: __11 packages__

   __110 pens and pencils__

7. Mark has 4 pages of sports cards. Each page has 3 rows with 3 cards in each row. How many sports cards are on all 4 pages?

   Hidden Question: How many sports cards are on 1 page?

   Answer to the Hidden Question: __9 sports cards__

   __36 sports cards__

8. John has \$8 and Bill has \$16. They want to buy a video game that costs \$20. Do they have enough money to buy the game? If so, how much money will they have left over?

   Hidden Question: How much money do John and Bill have in all?

   Answer to the Hidden Question: __\$24__

   __Yes; \$24 > \$20, \$24 − \$20 = \$4 left over__

 J4 (student p. 2) MDIS 2.0

Objective Students will answer hidden questions to solve two-step problems.
Vocabulary Hidden question

1 Conceptual Development
Use with Exercises 1–5.

In this lesson you will learn to find and answer hidden questions to solve two-step problems.

Have students read the problem at the top of the page and complete Exercises 1–3. *We need to find how many stickers in all Susan has left after she gives away 6 stickers. What do we need to find before we can answer that question?* How many stickers Susan has in both sticker collections *Some problems have a hidden question that must be answered before the original problem can be solved. A question that must be answered but that is not written is called a hidden question. What number sentence can you write to help answer the hidden question in Exercise 3?* 36 + 25 = 61 Then have students complete Exercises 4 and 5.

2 Practice **Use with Exercises 6–8.**

Explain to students that for each exercise, they must identify and solve the hidden question before they can solve the original problem.

Error Intervention If students have difficulty identifying hidden questions, have them review the **understand** and the **plan-and-solve** steps demonstrated in Exercises 1–4. Ask pointed questions about each problem to help students identify what needs to be answered first.

If You Have More Time Have pairs of students write two-step problems. Then have them exchange the problems with other pairs and solve.

3 Assessment

In this lesson students learned to solve two-step problems by first identifying and then answering hidden questions. Use the **Quick Check** problem to assess students' understanding.

Quick Check  **Formative** Assessment

Tamara has a photo album with 10 pages for photos. On each page, she places 3 rows with 2 pictures in each row. How many photos does she place in the album? Write and solve the hidden question. Then solve the problem. How many photos are on 1 page of the album?; 6 photos per page; 60 photos in the album

Intervention Lesson **J5**

Name ______

Multi-Step Problems

Intervention Lesson J5

Carmen bought 2 DVDs on sale for $21.99 each. She gave the clerk a $3 discount coupon and a $50 bill. The tax was $2.64. How much change should she receive?

Solve by answering 1 to 11.

Answer 1 and 2 to **understand** the problem.

1. What do you know from reading the problem?

   Carmen bought __2 DVDs__. Each DVD cost __$21.99__.

   Carmen gave the clerk a discount coupon worth __$3__.

   Carmen gave the clerk a __$50__ bill.

   Tax was __$2.64__.

2. What do you need to find?
   How much change did Carmen receive?

Answer 3 to 7 to **plan and solve** the problem.

3. How can you find how much change Carmen received?
   Subtract the total cost from $50.

4. Does the problem tell you the total cost? __no__

5. Do you have enough information to find the total cost? __yes__

"What is the total cost?" is the **hidden question** in the problem. You need to answer the hidden question before you can solve the problem.

 J5 (student p. 1) MDIS 2.0

Name ______

Multi-Step Problems (continued)

Intervention Lesson J5

6. How can you find the total cost?
   Add the cost of the DVDs and the tax. Then subtract the discount from the coupon.

7. Does the problem tell you the total cost of the two DVDs before tax and the discount? __no__

"What is the total cost of the two DVDS before tax and the discount?" is another **hidden question** in the problem.

8. What is the total cost of the two DVDS before tax and the discount? __$43.98__

9. What is the total cost of the two DVDS with tax and the discount? __$43.62__

10. How much change did Carmen receive? __$6.38__

Answer 11 to **check** your solution.

11. **Reasoning** Use an estimate to explain why your answer is reasonable.
    The DVDs cost about $22 each, or about $44 in all. The discount and tax are about the same, so the total cost with tax and discount was about $44. $50 − $44 = $6; Since $6.38 is close to $6, $6.38 is reasonable.

Use the table for Exercises 12 and 13.

Amusement Park Tickets	
Adults	$35.50
Junior tickets (under 48 in.)	$27.00
Starlight (after 5 P.M.)	$32.00

12. The Kim family bought 3 adult tickets and 2 junior tickets. What was the total cost of the tickets? __$160.50__

13. The Bondi family purchased 4 Starlight tickets for the amusement park. How much money did they save by buying 4 Starlight tickets rather than 4 adult tickets? __$14__

 J5 (student p. 2) MDIS 2.0

Objective Students will solve multi-step problems.
Vocabulary Discount coupon, tax

1 Conceptual Development

Use with Exercises 1–11.

In this lesson you will learn to solve multi-step problems.

Read the problem aloud with students. Explain that this is a multi-step problem because there are several steps required to answer the question. In this case, there is more than one hidden question. *What do you know after analyzing the problem?* How many DVDs Carmen bought, the cost of each DVD, the value of the discount coupon, the denomination of the bill that Carmen paid with, and the tax amount *What do you want to know?* How much change Carmen received *Was there any extra or missing information?* No Have students complete Exercises 1–2. *How do you calculate the amount of change?* Amount given for payment minus total cost *What do you need to calculate?* The total cost *To calculate the total cost, what do you need to know?* The total cost before the discount and tax Have students complete Exercises 3–10. *How will you estimate to see whether your answer is reasonable?* Sample answer: Round to make the numbers simpler Have students complete Exercise 11.

2 Practice **Use with Exercises 12–13.**

Remind students to identify and solve hidden questions as they work through the multi-step problems.

Error Intervention If students have difficulty solving multi-step problems, have them write the hidden questions before trying to solve the problem.

If You Have More Time Have students write a problem that has two hidden questions. Then have them trade with a partner and solve the problem.

3 Assessment

In this lesson students learned to solve multi-step problems. Use the **Quick Check** problem to assess students' understanding.

Quick Check

Henry bought 6 tickets for the banquet. Roberto bought 4 tickets for the banquet. The tickets were each $12. How much more did Henry spend than Roberto?
$24

Name ________________

Intervention Lesson J6

Make an Organized List

Materials 4 index cards cut in half to make 8 halves

Veronica is playing a game called *Guess the Number*. What are all the possible numbers that fit the clues shown on the right? How many numbers are there?

Clues
It is a 3-digit odd number.
The hundreds digit is less than 3.
The tens digit is greater than 6.
The ones digit is greater than 6.

Solve by answering 1 to 10.

Answer 1 to 5 to **understand** the problem.

1. What do you know from reading the problem?

   The number has 3 digits and is odd.

   The hundreds digit is less than 3.

   Both the tens and ones digits are greater than 6.

2. What do you need to find?
   What are all the possible numbers that fit the clues? How many numbers are there?

3. What digits can be in the hundreds place? 1 or 2

4. What digits can be in the tens place? 7, 8, 9

5. What digits can be in the ones place? 7 or 9

Answer 6 to 9 to **plan and solve** the problem.

6. Write the possible digits for each place on index cards.

Name ________________

Intervention Lesson J6

Make an Organized List (continued)

You can solve the problem by making an organized list.

Hundreds	Tens	Ones
1	7	7
1	7	9
1	8	7
1	8	9
1	9	7
1	9	9
2	7	7
2	7	9
2	8	7
2	8	9
2	9	7
2	9	9

7. Put the cards with the digits with the least value for each place together. What is one possible number?

   177

   This number is first in the list at the right.

8. Change the card for the ones digit and write another number in the list at the right. When you use all the ones cards, change the tens digit card to the next greatest digit and match it with each possible ones digit. Continue in this organized way until you have listed all the possible numbers.

9. How many numbers are possible? 12

Answer 10 to **look back** at how you solved the problem.

10. Did you answer the right question? yes

Complete each list to solve.

11. The cups used to sell drinks at the game come in packages of 100 or 10. How many different ways can 320 cups be bought?

    4 ways

Packages of 100	Packages of 10
3	2
2	12
1	22
0	32

12. You have black pants and tan pants. You have 3 shirts: black, red, and green. How many different outfits can you make?

    6 different outfits

B–B T–B
B–R T–R
B–G T–G

Objective Students will make an organized list to solve a problem.
Vocabulary Organized list
Materials 4 index cards cut in half to make 8 halves

1 Conceptual Development
Use with Exercises 1–10.

In this lesson you will learn to make an organized list to solve a problem.

Read the problem aloud with students. Explain that they will use an organized list to solve this problem. *What do you know after analyzing the problem?* The number has 3 digits, it is odd, the hundreds digit is less than 3, and both the tens digit and the ones digit are greater than 6. *What do you want to know?* How many possible numbers there are and what the possible numbers are Have students complete Exercises 1–5. *How will you use the cards?* To make possible numbers *How will you record possible numbers?* In the table that helps form an organized list Have students complete Exercise 6–10.

2 Practice Use with Exercises 11–12.

Discuss with students the importance of organizing their list. Explain that with an organized list, they can be sure they found each possibility and that they did not repeat anything.

Error Intervention If students have difficulty making an organized list, have them start with either the greatest or least value possible in the first column. They should not change this value until all the possibilities for the other columns have been found.

If You Have More Time Have students make a poster with their own clues for *Guess the Number.* Hang the posters in the room and let students try to solve each.

3 Assessment

In this lesson students learned to make an organized list to solve a problem. Use the **Quick Check** problem to assess students' understanding.

Quick Check 

Jorge has 10 cents. How many different combinations of coins might he have? 4

Name ______________________

Intervention Lesson J7

Make an Organized List

Carrie and Susi are playing a game. They spin the two spinners shown. If the spinners land on the same color, Carrie gets a point. Otherwise, Susi gets a point. How many combinations of two spins are possible? Is the game fair?

Red Blue Yellow

Solve by answering 1 to 8.

Answer 1 and 2 to **understand** the problem.

1. What do you know from reading the problem?

   Carrie gets a point if the spinners land on the same color.

   Susi gets a point if the spinners do not land on the same color.

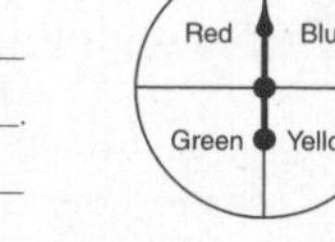

2. What do you need to find?

   How many combinations of two spins are possible? Is the game fair?

Answer 3 to 7 to **plan and solve** the problem.

You can solve the problem by making an organized list.

3. Use R for red, B for blue, Y for yellow, and G for green. Complete the list at the right.
4. How many combinations of spins are possible?

   12

RR	BR	YR
RB	BB	YB
RG	BG	YG
RY	BY	YY

Each combination is equally likely as any other.

5. For how many of the combinations does Carrie get a point? 3
6. For how many of the combinations does Susi get a point? 9
7. Is the game fair? no

Name ______________________

Intervention Lesson J7

Make an Organized List (continued)

Answer 8 to **look back** at how you solved the problem.

8. **Reasoning** Did you answer the right questions? Explain.

   Yes; there are 12 possible combinations and the game is not fair.

Solve each problem.

9. At a jewelry store, you can have your purchase gift-wrapped in silver, gold, or red paper with a white, pink, or blue ribbon. You can choose one color of paper and one color of ribbon. How many gift-wrap combinations are available?

   9 combinations

10. Mr. Johnson is making sandwiches. He has wheat bread and rye bread. He has ham and salami. He also has colby and cheddar cheese. Each sandwich will have one kind of bread, one kind of meat, and one kind of cheese. How many different kinds of sandwiches can he make?

    8 different kinds

11. Leslie has a penny, a nickel, and a dime in her pocket. If she picks out 2 coins, what amounts of money could she get?

    $0.06, $0.11, $0.15

12. Each child at Heather's party has chosen a sandwich and a drink. If there are 7 children at the party, can they each have a different lunch?

    Yes

Sandwiches	Drinks
Turkey Ham Tuna Peanut butter	Milk Juice

Objective Students will make an organized list to solve a problem.

Vocabulary Organized list

1 Conceptual Development

Use with Exercises 1–8.

In this lesson you will learn to make an organized list to solve a problem.

Read the problem aloud with students. Explain that they will use an organized list to solve this problem. *How do you know that an organized list is a good solution strategy?* Sample answer: You are trying to find how many different combinations there are. *What else do you want to know?* Whether the game is fair *How does Carrie get a point?* If the spinners land on the same color *How does Susi get a point?* If the spinners do not land on the same color Have students complete Exercises 1–3. *How will you represent each color in your list?* With the letter it starts with *How will you know whether the game is fair?* There will be an equal number of ways each girl can win. Have students complete Exercises 4–8.

2 Practice **Use with Exercises 9–12.**

Discuss with students the concept of a fair game. Have them speculate why it is important for a game to be fair.

Error Intervention

If students have difficulty finding the number of combinations by writing a list, have them use manipulatives to represent each option and make a physical list of the possible combinations.

If You Have More Time

Have students design a game and explain it to the class. The class will determine whether the game is fair.

3 Assessment

In this lesson students learned to make an organized list to solve a problem. Use the **Quick Check** problem to assess students' understanding.

Quick Check

Julie and Ben are playing a game where they roll two number cubes. If the sum is even, Julie gets a point. If the sum is odd, Ben gets a point. How many combinations of numbers on the number cubes are possible? Is this game fair? 36; yes

Name ______________________

Intervention Lesson J8

Analyze Given Information

Use the table at the right to solve the problem.

Tim and Bob are looking for rocks for a science project. Tim finds a rock that weighs 2 pounds, and Bob finds a rock that weighs 30 ounces. Who found the heavier rock? Explain.

1 foot = 12 inches
1 yard = 3 feet
1 pound = 16 ounces

Solve by answering 1 to 6.

Answer 1 and 2 to **understand** the problem.

1. What do you know from reading the problem?

   Tim's rock weighs __2__ pounds.

   Bob's rock weighs __30__ ounces.

2. What do you need to find?
   Sample answer: Whether Tim or Bob found the heavier rock

Answer 3 to 6 to **plan and solve** the problem.

3. You can compare both weights in ounces. Look at the information in the table to help. How many ounces are in 1 pound? __16__ ounces
4. Tim's rock weighs 2 pounds. You know how many ounces are in 1 pound. So, how many ounces are in 2 pounds? __32__ ounces
5. Show how much each rock weighs in ounces.

   Tim's rock weighs __32__ ounces.

   Bob's rock weighs __30__ ounces.

6. Compare the weights of the rocks in ounces. Who found the heavier rock? Explain.
   Sample answer: Tim found the heavier rock. 32 > 30

Name ______________________

Intervention Lesson J8

Analyze Given Information (continued)

Answer 7 to **look back** at how you solved the problem.

7. Explain how using the table helped you to find the correct answer.
   Sample answer: I wanted the weights to be the same unit so I could compare. I used the table to work out the number of ounces in 2 pounds. Then I could compare the weights in ounces.

Use the figure at the right to answer 8 and 9.

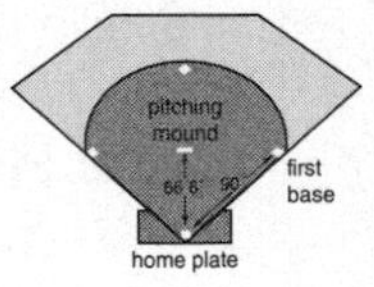

8. During a baseball game, a catcher throws a baseball from home plate to first base as shown to the right. How many yards did the catcher throw the baseball?
   __30 yards__
9. During a baseball game, a pitcher throws a baseball from the pitching mound to home plate as shown to the right. How many inches did the pitcher throw the ball?
   __798 inches__

Answer 10 and 11 using the picture at the right.

A square has 4 equal sides as shown at the right.

9 inches

10. What is the perimeter of the square in feet? __3 feet__
11. What is the perimeter of the square in yards? __1 yard__

Use the following information to answer 12.

The Smith family drives for 3 hours and 40 minutes on the first day of the family's trip and 4 hours and 20 minutes on the second day of the family's trip. There are 60 minutes in an hour.

12. How many hours did the family drive in all? __8 hours__

Objective Students will use given information to solve problems involving measurement conversions.
Vocabulary Yard, foot, inch, pound, ounce

❶ Conceptual Development
Use with Exercises 1–7.

In this lesson you will learn to use information to convert measurements and solve problems.

Have students read the problem and the conversion table at the top of the page. Revisit the terms *yard, foot, inch, pound,* and *ounce* as needed. Have students complete Exercise 1. *You know that 30 is greater than 2. Does this mean you know which rock is heavier?* No *Why not?* The units are different. *What does the information in the table show?* How many of one unit is equal to another unit *How could this help you to compare the weights?* I can convert one unit to be the same as the other unit so that I can compare like units to see which rock weighs more. Have students complete Exercises 3–7.

❷ Practice Use with Exercises 8–12.

Explain that the information students need to solve the problems will be found in the diagrams as well as the word problems. Students can also refer back to the conversion table on p. 1 of the SE.

Error Intervention If students have difficulty converting measurements, have them make a table showing the units they want to convert, for example: *3 feet = 1 yard, 6 feet = 2 yards, 9 feet = 3 yards,* etc.

If You Have More Time Have students solve the following problem and explain their methods: *Jane measured a length of 53 yards. Riaz measured a length that is 9 feet longer than Jane's length. How long was the length Riaz measured in yards?* 56 yards

❸ Assessment

In this lesson students learned to use given information to convert measurements and solve problems. Use the **Quick Check** problem to assess students' understanding.

Quick Check 

If you know that 1 foot = 12 inches, how can you find how many inches are in 8 feet? Sample answer: Multiply $8 \times 12 = 96$. There are 96 inches in 8 feet.

DRAW A PICTURE AND WRITE A NUMBER SENTENCE

Intervention Lesson **J9**

Name ______________________

Intervention Lesson J9

Draw a Picture and Write a Number Sentence

For the science project, Ms. Trapp needs 27 paper towel rolls for each of her 3 classes. How many rolls does she need in all?

Solve by answering 1 to 7.

Answer 1 and 2 to **understand** the problem.

1. What do you know from reading the problem?

   Ms. Trapp needs <u>27</u> paper towel rolls for each class.

   Ms. Trapp has <u>3</u> classes.

2. What do you need to find?
   How many paper towel rolls does Ms. Trapp need in all?

Answer 3 to 5 to **plan and solve** the problem.

You can solve the problem by drawing a picture and writing a number sentence.

3. Complete the picture at the right to show what you know.

? paper towel rolls

27	27	27

Paper towel rolls needed for each

4. Write a number sentence to solve.

   <u>3 × 27 = 81</u>

5. How many paper towel rolls does Ms. Trapp need in all? <u>81</u> paper towel rolls

Answer 6 and 7 to **look back and check** how you solved the problem.

6. Did you answer the right question? <u>yes</u>

Name ______________________

Intervention Lesson J9

Draw a Picture and Write a Number Sentence (continued)

7. **Reasoning** Use estimation to explain why your answer is reasonable.
   Sample answer: Ms. Trapp needs about 30 paper towel rolls for each class and 3 × 30 = 90. Since 81 is close to 90, the answer of 81 is reasonable.

Draw a picture and write a number sentence to solve each problem.

8. The catering company ordered 16 tablecloths. They also ordered 8 times as many napkins. How many napkins did they order?

tablecloths	16								
napkins	16	16	16	16	16	16	16	16	8 times as many

? napkins in all

Number sentence: <u>8 × 16 = 128</u> <u>128</u> napkins

9. Mr. and Mrs. Gordon have 11 grandsons and 8 granddaughters. How many grandchildren do the Gordons have?

?

11	8

Number sentence: <u>11 + 8 = 19</u> <u>19</u> grandchildren

10. Yul bought a case for his CDs. Each page in the case holds 4 CDs. The case has 24 pages. How many CDs can the case hold?

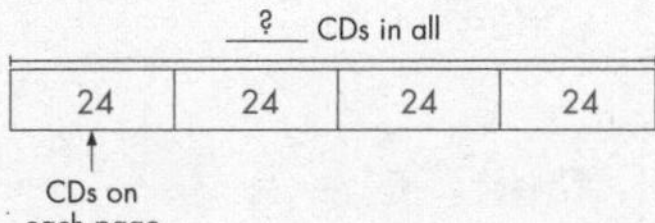

CDs on each page

Number sentence: <u>4 × 24 = 96</u> <u>96</u> CDs

11. Amy and Todd have blown up 34 balloons for a birthday party. Amy has blown up 18 balloons. How many did Todd blow up?

34

18	?

Number sentence: <u>34 − 18 = 16</u> <u>16</u> balloons

Objective Students will draw a picture and write a number sentence to solve a problem.
Vocabulary Number sentence

1 Conceptual Development

Use with Exercises 1–7.

In this lesson you will learn to draw a picture and write a number sentence to solve a problem.

Read the problem aloud with students. Explain that they will draw a picture and write a number sentence to solve this problem. *What information do you know?* The number of paper towel rolls per class and the number of classes *What do you want to know?* How many paper towel rolls are needed in all Have students complete Exercises 1–2. *What does each rectangle represent?* The number of rolls needed for each class *What number should go in each rectangle?* 27 *What number sentence represents this picture?* 27 × 3 = ? *How can you estimate your answer to check for reasonableness?* Sample answer: 25 × 3 = 75, which is close to 81. Have students complete Exercises 3–7.

2 Practice Use with Exercises 8–11.

Help students connect different pictures to addition and multiplication. Draw pictures for each operation to show what it would look like.

Error Intervention If students have difficulty drawing a picture, remind them to use rectangles to represent objects. Tell them that their pictures should not be elaborate.

If You Have More Time Give students a drawing and have them write the problem and the number sentence they would use to solve it.

3 Assessment

In this lesson students learned to draw a picture and write a number sentence to solve a problem. Use the **Quick Check** problem to assess students' understanding.

Quick Check 

Draw a picture and write a number sentence to solve: Mrs. Bailey has 13 fish and 4 hamsters. How many pets does she have?

? pets

13	4

13 + 4 = ?; 17

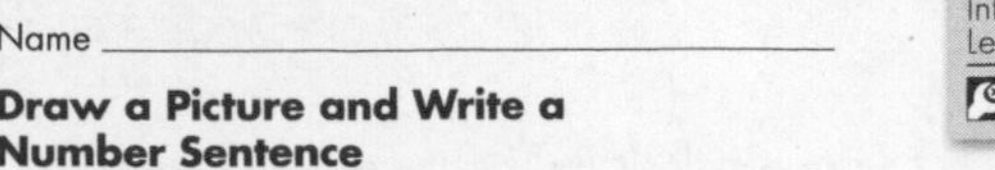

Name ______________________

Draw a Picture and Write a Number Sentence

Intervention Lesson **J10**

The pet store ordered 24 hamsters. They put the hamsters in 6 different cages. If each cage had the same number of hamsters, how many hamsters were put in each cage?

Solve by answering 1 to 6.

Answer 1 and 2 to **understand** the problem.

1. What do you know from reading the problem?

   The pet store ordered _24_ hamsters.

   The pet store put the hamsters in _6_ different cages, with the same number of hamsters in each cage.

2. What do you need to find?

   How many hamsters were put in each cage?

Answer 3 to 5 to **plan and solve** the problem.

You can solve the problem by drawing a picture and writing a number sentence.

3. Complete the picture at the right to show what you know.

_24_ hamsters

?	?	?	?	?	?

Hamsters in each cage

4. Write a number sentence to solve.

   $24 \div 6 = 4$

5. How many hamsters were put in each cage? _4_ hamsters

Answer 6 to **look back** at how you solved the problem.

6. Did you answer the right question? _yes_

 J10 (student p. 1) MDIS 2.0

Name ______________________

Draw a Picture and Write a Number Sentence (continued)

Intervention Lesson **J10**

Draw a picture and write a number sentence to solve each problem.

7. The florist ordered 36 vases. The vases were packaged 4 to a box. How many boxes were delivered to the florist?

   Number sentence:

   $36 \div 4 = 9$

   _9_ boxes

   _36_ vases

4	- - - - - - →

   Vases in each box; _?_ boxes

8. Johnston has 6 rolls of quarters. Each roll has 40 quarters. How many quarters does Johnston have?

   Number sentence:

   $6 \times 40 = 240$

   _240_ quarters

   _?_ quarters in all

40	40	40	40	40	40

   Quarters in each roll

9. Coach Yellowstone ordered 40 basketballs. He put them in 5 different bins. If each bin had the same number of basketballs, how many basketballs were put in each bin?

   Number sentence:

   $40 \div 5 = 8$

   _8_ basketballs

   _40_ basketballs

?	?	?	?	?

   Basketballs in each bin

10. Emily scored 7 times as many points on the video game as Roberta. Roberta scored 86 points. How many points did Emily score?

    Number sentence:

    $7 \times 86 = 602$

    _602_ points

Roberta	86							
Emily	86	86	86	86	86	86	86	7 times as many

    _?_ points

 J10 (student p. 2) MDIS 2.0

Objective Students will draw a picture and write a number sentence to solve a problem.
Vocabulary Number sentence

1 Conceptual Development
Use with Exercises 1–6.

In this lesson you will learn to draw a picture and write a number sentence to solve a problem.

Explain to students that they will draw a picture and write a number sentence to solve this problem. *What do you know about how many hamsters will go in each cage?* An equal number *What are you trying to find?* The number of hamsters in each cage Have students complete Exercises 1–2. *Why are there six rectangles?* There are six cages. *What operation separates items into equal groups?* Division *What number sentence will help you solve this problem?* $24 \div 6 = ?$ Have students complete Exercises 3–6.

2 Practice **Use with Exercises 7–10.**

Show students that pictures can be used to solve addition, subtraction, multiplication, and division problems.

Error Intervention If students have difficulty writing a number sentence for their picture, ask them how they would solve the problem. Then have them translate their words into a number sentence.

If You Have More Time Have students draw a picture that could be used to solve a problem. Then have them trade it with a partner and write a real-world problem to match their partner's picture.

3 Assessment

In this lesson students learned to draw a picture and write a number sentence to solve a problem. Use the **Quick Check** problem to assess students' understanding.

Quick Check 

Draw a picture and write a number sentence to solve: Mr. Trent has four times as many novels as biographies. He has 11 biographies. How many novels does he have? $4 \times 11 = ?$; 44; Check students' bar diagrams.

DRAW A STRIP DIAGRAM AND WRITE AN EQUATION

Intervention Lesson **J11**

Name ______________________

Intervention Lesson **J11**

Draw a Strip Diagram and Write an Equation

Coach Henderson marked off the path he wants his players to run. The path is $\frac{7}{10}$ of a mile. Paulo already ran $\frac{4}{10}$ of a mile. How far does Paulo have left to run?

Solve by answering 1 to 7.

Answer 1 and 2 to **understand** the problem.

1. What do you know from reading the problem?
   The path is $\frac{7}{10}$ of a mile long.
   Paulo already ran $\frac{4}{10}$ of a mile.
2. What do you need to find?
   How far does Paulo have left to run?

Answer 3 to 5 to **plan and solve** the problem.

You can solve the problem by drawing a strip diagram and writing a an equation.

3. Complete the strip diagram at the right to show what you know.
4. Write an equation to solve.
   $\frac{7}{10} - \frac{4}{10} = n$

$\frac{7}{10}$ of a mile

$\frac{4}{10}$	n

Part already ran

5. How far does Paulo have left to run? $\frac{3}{10}$ of a mile

Answer 6 and 7 to **check** that your solution is reasonable.

6. Should the distance Paulo has left to run be less than $\frac{7}{10}$ of a mile? yes
7. Is $\frac{3}{10}$ less than $\frac{7}{10}$? yes

Name ______________________

Intervention Lesson **J11**

Draw a Strip Diagram and Write an Equation (continued)

Draw a strip diagram and write an equation to solve each problem.

8. The road repair crew is resurfacing 1 mile of roadway. They finished $\frac{5}{12}$ mile yesterday, and $\frac{4}{12}$ mile today. What fraction of a mile have they resurfaced?
   Equation: $\frac{5}{12} + \frac{4}{12} = t$
   $\frac{3}{4}$ mile

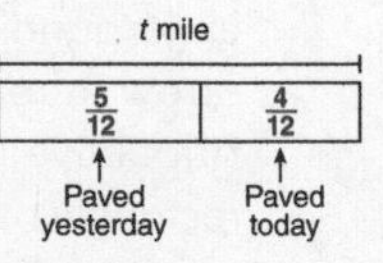

9. Maykala blew up 24 balloons for the Fourth of July celebration. She blew up the same number of balloons of each color: red, white, and blue. How many red balloons did she blow up?
   Equation: $24 \div 3 = b$
   8 red balloons

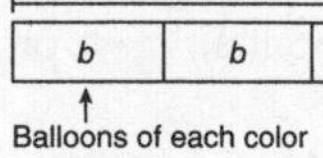

10. Benny ran the first $\frac{3}{8}$ of the nature trail, walked the next $\frac{4}{8}$ of the trail, and skipped the last $\frac{1}{8}$ of the trail. How much more of the trail did Benny walk than skip?
    Equation: $\frac{4}{8} - \frac{1}{8} = t$
    $\frac{3}{8}$ more of the trail

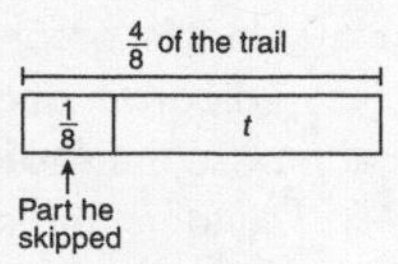

11. Joe divided 56 dance students into groups of 8. How many dance groups are there?
    Equation: $56 \div 8 = g$
    7 groups

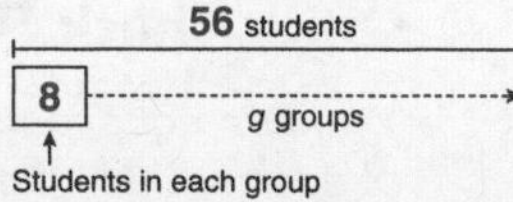

Objective Students will draw a strip diagram and write an equation to solve a problem.
Vocabulary Strip diagram, equation

1 Conceptual Development

Use with Exercises 1–7.

In this lesson you will learn to draw a strip diagram and write an equation to solve a problem.

Read the problem aloud with students. Explain that they will draw a strip diagram and write an equation to solve this problem. *What information do you know?* How long the path is and how far Paulo has run *What are you trying to find?* How much farther he has to run Have students complete Exercises 1–2. *What represents the total length of the path in the strip diagram shown?* The length of the two rectangles together *What does the first rectangle represent?* How far he has already run ($\frac{4}{10}$) *What does the second rectangle represent?* How far he has to run *Why is there an n in this rectangle?* We do not know how far he has to run *What operation will you use to find the distance he has left to run?* Subtraction Have students complete Exercises 3–7.

2 Practice Use with Exercises 8–11.

Make sure students recall how to add, subtract, multiply, and divide fractions.

Error Intervention If students have difficulty drawing a strip diagram, give them a page with samples for each kind: addition, subtraction, multiplication, and division.

If You Have More Time Have students explain how they know what kind of equation to write for each exercise.

3 Assessment

In this lesson students learned to draw a strip diagram and write an equation to solve a problem. Use the **Quick Check** problem to assess students' understanding.

Quick Check

Draw a strip diagram and write an equation to solve: Ian cleaned $\frac{1}{8}$ of his room yesterday and $\frac{5}{8}$ of his room today. How much of his room is clean? $\frac{1}{8} + \frac{5}{8} = ?$; $\frac{6}{8}$ or $\frac{3}{4}$; Check students' strip diagrams.

DRAW A STRIP DIAGRAM AND WRITE AN EQUATION

Name ______________________

Intervention Lesson J12

Draw a Strip Diagram and Write an Equation

Rachel has 108 pictures to put in a photo album. Each page in the album holds 8 pictures. How many pages does Rachel need to use?

Solve by answering 1 to 7.

Answer 1 and 2 to **understand** the problem.

1. What do you know from reading the problem?

   Rachel has 108 pictures to put in a photo album.

   Each page holds 8 pictures.

2. What do you need to find?
   How many pages does Rachel need to use?

Answer 3 to 6 to **plan and solve** the problem.

You can solve the problem by drawing a strip diagram and writing an equation.

3. Complete the strip diagram below to show what you know.

   108 pictures

   [8] - - - - - - - - p pages - - - - - - - - →

   Pictures on each page

4. Write an equation to solve.

   $108 \div 8 = p$

5. What do you get for the value of p? 13 R 4

6. How many pages does Rachel need to use? 14

Answer 7 to **look back** at your solution.

7. **Reasoning** Explain why Rachel needs to use 14 pages.
   13 pages are full and the last page has 4 pictures.

 J12 (student p. 1) MDIS 2.0

Name ______________________

Intervention Lesson J12

Draw a Strip Diagram and Write an Equation (continued)

Write an equation and solve each problem.

8. There are 236 people invited to a charity banquet. Each table will seat 8 people. How many tables are needed to seat everyone?

   Equation: $236 \div 8 = t$ Solution: 30 tables

9. Jon has a rock collection. The rocks are stored in cases that hold 16 rocks in each case. He has 185 rocks in his collection. How many cases can Jon completely fill?

   Equation: $185 \div 16 = c$ Solution: 11 cases

10. During a foggy day, visibility in Tonkawa was $\frac{5}{6}$ mile. The visibility in Marland was $\frac{2}{6}$ mile. What was the difference in the visibility of the two towns?

    Equation: $\frac{5}{6} - \frac{2}{6} = m$ Solution: $\frac{1}{2}$ mile

11. A book and a \$2.75 magazine cost \$14.50 together. How much does the book cost?

    Equation: $b + 2.75 = 14.50$ or $14.50 - 2.75 = b$ Solution: \$11.75

12. Phillip paid \$18.75 for a soccer ball on sale. What was the price before the sale?

    Equation: $p - 2.50 = 18.75$ or $18.75 + 2.50 = p$ Solution: \$21.25

13. Tammy earns \$8 per hour. She earned \$480 last month. How many hours did she work?

    Equation: $480 \div 8 = t$ Solution: 60 hours

 J12 (student p. 2) MDIS 2.0

Objective Students will draw a strip diagram and write an equation to solve a problem.
Vocabulary Strip diagram, equation

1 Conceptual Development
Use with Exercises 1–7.

In this lesson you will learn to draw a strip diagram and write an equation to solve a problem.

Read the problem aloud with students. Explain that they will draw a strip diagram and write an equation to solve this problem. *What information do you know?* How many pictures Rachel has and how many pictures each page in the photo album holds *What are you trying to find?* How many pages she needs to use Have students complete Exercises 1–2. *What represents the total length of the photo album in the strip diagram shown?* The total number of pictures she has *What does the rectangle represent?* The number of pictures on a page *Why is there an arrow for p pages instead of a number of rectangles?* We do not know how many pages yet, so we cannot draw a rectangle for each page. Have students complete Exercises 3–7.

2 Practice Use with Exercises 8–13.

Review division with remainders and interpreting those remainders.

Error Intervention If students have difficulty understanding why they sometimes have to use an arrow to represent the number of rectangles in the strip, have them try to draw the right number of rectangles. They will see that they do not know how many to draw without solving the problem.

If You Have More Time Have students make up their own photo album problems.

3 Assessment

In this lesson students learned to draw a strip diagram and write an equation to solve a problem. Use the **Quick Check** problem to assess students' understanding.

Quick Check  **Formative** Assessment

Write an equation to solve: There are 6 students sitting at each table in the classroom. There are 33 students in the class. How many tables are needed?
$33 \div 6 = 5$ R3; 6 tables

TRY, CHECK, AND REVISE

Name ______

Try, Check, and Revise

Intervention Lesson J13

The Koch family bought 5 tickets at the prices shown on the sign at the right. The family spent $36. How many tickets of each type did the family buy?

TICKETS	
Adults	$9 each
Children	$6 each

Solve by answering 1 to 8.

Answer 1 to 3 to **understand** the problem.

1. What do you know from reading the problem?
   The Koch family bought 5 tickets and spent 36.
2. What do you know from reading the sign?
   Adult's tickets cost $9 and children's tickets cost $6.
3. What do you need to find?
   How many tickets of each type did the Koch family buy?

Answer 4 to 7 to **plan and solve** the problem.

You can solve the problem by using the strategy Try, Check, and Revise.

4. Suppose you guess that the Koch family bought 3 adult and 2 children's tickets. Check your guess. How much do 3 adult's and 2 children's tickets cost? $39
5. Is the cost too high, too low, or just right? too high
6. How can you change your guess to get a lower total?
   Increase the number of children's tickets and decrease the adult ones.
7. Revise the guess and try again until the total cost is $36. How many tickets of each type did the Koch family buy?
   They bought 2 adult's and 3 children's tickets.

 J13 (student p. 1) MDIS 2.0

Name ______

Try, Check, and Revise (continued)

Intervention Lesson J13

Answer 8 to **look back** at how you solved the problem.

8. Explain how to use Try, Check, and Revise to solve a problem.
   First you guess an answer to try. Then you check to see if the answer is the solution. If it isn't, you revise your guess to make it better. Then you check the new solution. You repeat this process until you get the right answer.

For Exercises 9 to 11, use the table at the right.

Camping Town	
Sleeping bag	$10
Flashlight	$3
Lantern	$5
Canteen	$4
Dried food	$2

9. Karen bought 2 different items. She spent $8. Which items did she buy?
   Karen bought a flashlight and lantern.
10. Jake bought 3 different items. He spent a total of $15. Which items did he buy?
    Jake bought a sleeping bag, flashlight, and dried food.
11. Adam spent $19 at Camping Town on 4 items. Two of his items were the same. What did he buy?
    Adam bought a sleeping bag, lantern, and 2 dried foods.

Solve each problem.

12. Gina has twice as many goldfish as zebra fish. Together, there are 42 of these two types of fish in her tank. How many goldfish and zebra fish does she have?
    Gina has 14 zebra fish and 28 goldfish in her tank.
13. Josh delivers pizza. In his money pouch are 6 bills worth $18. If he only has $1 and $5 bills, how many of each bill does he have?
    Josh has three $5 bills and three $1 bills.

 J13 (student p. 2) MDIS 2.0

Objective Students will use the Try, Check, and Revise strategy to solve a problem.
Vocabulary Revise

1 Conceptual Development
Use with Exercises 1–8.

In this lesson you will learn to use the Try, Check, and Revise strategy to solve a problem.

Explain that students will use the Try, Check, and Revise strategy to solve a problem and check their answers. *What information do you know?* How many tickets the Koch family bought, how much the family spent, and the ticket costs *What are you trying to find?* How many of each type of ticket the family bought Have students complete Exercises 1–3. Discuss the first try with students. *How will you revise your answer for the next try?* Use fewer adult tickets *How many tries, checks, and revisions did it take you to get the correct answer?* Answers will vary. Emphasize that it is OK for a try to be incorrect. Have students complete Exercises 4–8.

2 Practice **Use with Exercises 9–13.**

Encourage students to record all of their work. Each try will help them revise their answers more effectively.

Error Intervention If students have difficulty understanding how to revise their answers, have them evaluate the problem with their answer. If the answer is too low, they need to find a way to increase it. If it is too high, they need to find a way to decrease it.

If You Have More Time Have students write their own camping problem and then trade it with a partner. Have partners use the Try, Check, and Revise strategy to solve the problem.

3 Assessment

In this lesson students learned to use the Try, Check, and Revise strategy to solve a problem. Use the **Quick Check** problem to assess students' understanding.

Quick Check  **Formative** Assessment

Juanita has twice as many animated movies as non-animated movies. She has 48 movies in all. How many of each type of movie does she have?
16 nonanimated, 32 animated

Name ______________________________

Try, Check, and Revise

Intervention Lesson **J14**

Materials place-value blocks, 24 unit cubes for each student

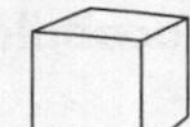

Sylvia has 24 small boxes that are each in the shape of a cube. She needs to arrange them to form a larger box in the shape of a rectangular prism. How many different rectangular prisms can Sylvia make with the 24 cubes?

Solve by answering 1 to 7.

Answer 1 and 2 to **understand** the problem.

1. What do you know from reading the problem?

   Sylvia has ___24___ small boxes, each the shape of a ___cube___.

2. What do you need to find?
   How many different rectangular prisms can Sylvia make with 24 cubes?

Answer 3 to 6 to **plan and solve** the problem.

You can solve the problem by using the strategy Try, Check, and Revise.

3. Use the blocks to try a height of 1 and a width of 1. Is it possible to make a rectangular prism? ___yes___

4. What are the prism's dimensions? 1 by 1 by ___24___

5. Use the blocks to try a height of 1 and a width of 2, then a height of 1 and a width of 3, and so on. Then try a height of 2 and a width of 2, a height of 2 and a width of 3 and so on. List all the dimensions that work. Consider 1 by 2 by 12 the same as 2 by 1 by 12.
   1 by 2 by 12; 1 by 3 by 8; 1 by 4 by 6; 2 by 2 by 6; 2 by 3 by 4

Name ______________________________

Try, Check, and Revise (continued)

Intervention Lesson **J14**

6. How many different rectangular prisms can Sylvia make with the 24 cubes? ___6___

Answer 7 to **look back** at how you solved the problem.

7. Did you answer the right question? ___yes___

Solve each problem.

8. Angus has 22 feet of flower-bed edging. The rectangular shaped flower bed he made is 5 feet longer than it is wide. What are the dimensions of his flower bed?

   ___3 feet wide and 8 ft long___

9. Genia has 10 coins that consist of dimes and nickels. She has a total of $0.60. How many does she have of each coin?

   ___2 dimes and 8 nickels___

10. During a visit to the zoo, Mary counted 32 legs. The only animals in the exhibit were ostriches and giraffes. How many of each animal were in the exhibit?

    ___4 ostriches and 6 giraffes___

11. Nadine wants to build a patio that has an area of 36 square yards. However, she wants the patio to have the smallest perimeter possible. What dimensions should she build her patio?

    ___6 yards by 6 yards___

12. Simone bought 20 CDs and paid $149. How many new and how many used CDs did she buy?

    ___7 new and 13 used___

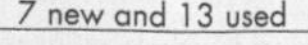

13. A group spent $180 for 11 tickets. How many adult tickets and how many child tickets did the group buy?

    ___8 adult and 3 child___

TICKETS
adults $18 each
children $12 each

Objective Students will use the Try, Check, and Revise strategy to solve a problem.
Materials Place-value blocks, 24 unit cubes for each student

1 Conceptual Development

Use with Exercises 1–7.

In this lesson you will learn to use the Try, Check, and Revise strategy to solve a problem.

Have students read aloud the word problem. Explain that they will use the Try, Check, and Revise strategy to solve the problem and check their answers. *What information do you know?* Sylvia has 24 small boxes that are each in the shape of a cube. *What are you trying to find?* The number of rectangular prisms that she can make with 24 cubes Have students complete Exercises 1–2. Tell students they will be using their cubes to solve the word problem. Have students follow the steps in Exercises 3–5 to solve the problem and then complete Exercises 6–7.

2 Practice **Use with Exercises 8–13.**

Remind students that it is unlikely that they will get the correct answer on the first try and that the number of tries is not an indicator of how well the problem was done. Emphasize that the correct answer is the goal.

Error Intervention If students have difficulty getting started, have them write what they know from reading the problem and what they need to find out, similar to the first two exercises. Then have them use the cubes to try possible answers. For Exercise 8, for example, have them begin with a width of 1 foot and a length of 5 + 1 feet and assess.

If You Have More Time Have students write out the steps they used to solve Exercise 8.

3 Assessment

In this lesson students learned to use the Try, Check, and Revise strategy to solve a problem. Use the **Quick Check** problem to assess students' understanding.

Quick Check 

Small drinks cost $1, and large drinks cost $2. Paulo spent $8 and got 5 drinks. How many large drinks and how many small drinks did he buy? 3 large drinks, 2 small drinks

SOLVE A SIMPLER PROBLEM

Name ____________________

Intervention Lesson J15

Solve a Simpler Problem

A diagram of a flower garden in the city park is shown on the right. The garden is made of rose bushes and marigolds. The shaded part of the figure shows the part of the garden that is marigolds. What is the area of the shaded part of the flower garden?

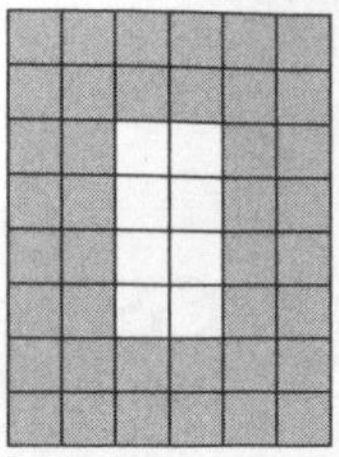

□ = 1 square yard

Solve by answering 1 to 6.

Answer 1 and 2 to **understand** the problem.

1. What do you know from reading the problem?

   The diagram shows a garden. The shaded part shows the part with marigolds.

   The rest of the garden has __roses__.

2. What do you need to find?
   What is the area of the shaded part of the flower garden?

Answer 3 to 5 to **plan and solve** the problem.

You can solve the problem by solving two simpler problems first.

3. What is the area of the whole garden?

   __8__ × __6__ = __48__

4. What is the area of the part that is not shaded?

   __4__ × __2__ = __8__

5. The area of the shaded part is the whole area minus the part that is not shaded. What is the area of the shaded part?

   __48__ − __8__ = __40__ square yards

 J15 (student p. 1) MDIS 2.0

Name ____________________

Intervention Lesson J15

Solve a Simpler Problem (continued)

Answer 6 to **look back** at how you solved the problem.

6. Explain how to use Solving a Simpler Problem to solve a problem.
   Sample answer: First you solve part of the problem, that is easier to solve than the whole problem. Then you use the answers you get to solve the original problem.

Solve each problem.

Use the grid at the right for Exercises 7 and 8. Be careful, arrows show one-way streets.

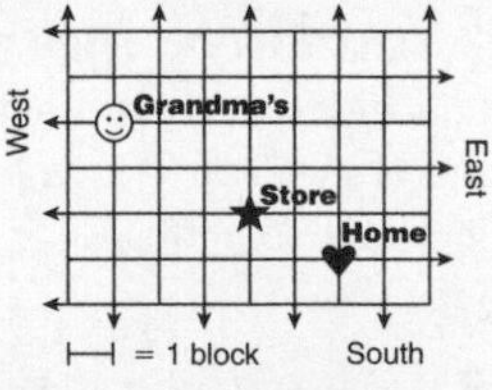

7. Find the distance (the number of blocks) from home to the store and then to Grandma's.

   __8 blocks__

8. Sara started from home, drove 5 blocks north, 3 blocks west, and 4 blocks south, but she still needed to go to the store. How many blocks was she from the store?

   __1 block__

Gloria tiled her bathroom floor. She used white and gray tiles as shown at the right. Use the diagram for Exercises 9 and 10.

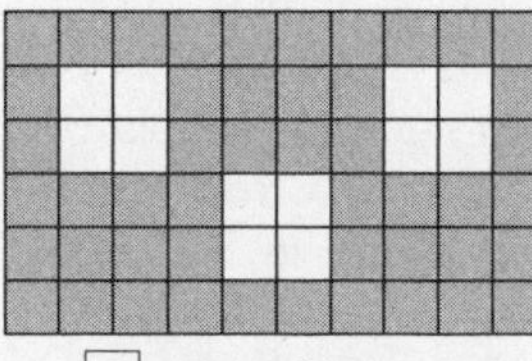

□ = 1 square foot

9. What is the gray area?

   __48 ft²__

10. How much greater is the gray area than the white area?

   __36 ft²__

 J15 (student p. 2) MDIS 2.0

Objective Students will use the strategy of solving a simpler problem.

1 Conceptual Development

Use with Exercises 1–6.

In this lesson you will learn the strategy of solving a simpler problem.

Have students read the word problem and look at the diagram. *How large is each square in the diagram?* 1 square yard *What are you asked to find?* The area of the shaded part of the flower garden Have students complete Exercises 1–2. *How can you find the area?* Multiply the length by the width Have students complete Exercises 3–5. Ask students to explain aloud how to solve a simpler problem and then have them complete Exercise 6.

2 Practice Use with Exercises 7–10.

Remind students that they can solve a problem by solving the simpler parts of the problem first and then using those solutions to solve the original problem.

Error Intervention If students have difficulty solving Exercise 7, have them use their finger to begin at Home and then move north one block. Ask how many blocks they have just gone and have students write a tally. Have them move west 2 blocks and complete their tally. Encourage them to use this method to solve Exercise 8 if needed.

If You Have More Time Have students use the grid in Exercise 7 to write and solve their own problem and then exchange it with a partner to solve.

3 Assessment

In this lesson students learned the strategy of solving a simpler problem. Use the **Quick Check** problem to assess students' understanding.

Quick Check

Solve using the grid from Exercise 7: Sara started from Home and went 2 blocks east before going to Grandma's. How many blocks was she from Grandma's? 10 blocks

Name ______________________

Intervention Lesson J16

Use Representations

The students in Mrs. Nolan's class each collected cans of food to donate. The results are shown in the dot plot at the right.

Cans of Food Collected

0 5 10 15 20 25

Cans Per Student

Use the information in the dot plot to answer 1 to 4.

1. How many students collected 15 cans? 4 students
2. How many more students collected 10 cans than 20 cans? 5 students
3. How many students collected more than 15 cans? 2 students
4. How many cans were collected in all? 205 cans

Steve kept track of the number of minutes he spent working on homework for the last 10 days. His data is listed in the stem-and-leaf plot at the right.

Time Spent on Homework	
Stem	Leaf
1	0 5 7
2	1 2 4
3	0 6
4	0 3
Key: 1|5 = 15 minutes	

Use the stem-and-leaf plot to answer 5 to 7.

5. What is the least amount of time Steve spent working on his homework? 10 minutes
6. What is the greatest amount of time Steve spent working on his homework? 43 minutes
7. How many more minutes did Steve spend on his homework for the greatest time spent compared to the least time spent? 33 minutes

 J16 (student p. 1) MDIS 2.0

Name ______________________

Intervention Lesson J16

Use Representations (continued)

The data shown in the dot plot at the right was collected from the Jeffersonville Fishing Derby.

Jeffersonville Fishing Derby

0 2 4 6 8 10 12

Fish

Use the dot plot to answer 8 to 11.

8. What was the least number of fish caught? 2 fish
9. What was the greatest number of fish caught? 12 fish
10. How many more people caught 10 fish than 6 fish? 3 fishermen
11. Did more people catch less than 6 fish or more than 6 fish? Explain. More than 6 fish; 8 people caught less than 6 fish, and 10 people caught more than 6 fish. $8 < 10$

Mrs. Wilson collected the scores from her students' latest test. Their scores are shown in the stem-and-leaf plot at the right.

Test Scores	
Stem	Leaf
6	0 3 3 7 7
7	2 2 5 5 8
8	1 4 4 6 9 9 9
9	1 5 8
Key: 7|5 = 75 points	

Use the stem-and-leaf plot to answer 12 to 15.

12. What was the highest test score? 98 points
13. What was the lowest test score? 60 points
14. What is the difference between the most points scored and the least points scored on the test? 38 points
15. How many students took the test? 20 students

 J16 (student p. 2) MDIS 2.0

Objective Students will use dot plots and stem-and-leaf plots to interpret data.
Vocabulary Dot plot, stem-and-leaf plot

1 Conceptual Development

Use with Exercises 1–7.

In this lesson you will learn to use dot plots and stem-and-leaf plots to interpret data.

Have students read the problem and use the dot plot. Have students complete Exercise 1. *What does each dot stand for?* 1 student *Look at the column of dots that represents 15 cans. How many dots are in that column?* 4 Have students use the dot plot to complete Exercises 2–4. *How can you find the total number of cans collected?* Count the number of dots in a column and multiply it by the number of cans it represents. Add each product. Have students read the "homework" problem and use the stem-and-leaf plot. *What are the times represented in the plot?* 10, 15, 17, 21, 22, 24, 30, 36, 40, 43 Have students use this data to complete Exercises 5–7.

2 Practice Use with Exercises 8–15.

Remind students that each part of a plot represents a piece of data. Students should use the data in the plots to answer the questions.

Error Intervention If students have difficulty answering *more than* and *less than* questions, have them highlight the data that is applicable. For example, highlight the first two columns of the dot plot for the people who caught less than 6 fish.

If You Have More Time Have students make their own word problems that can be answered using one of the plots. Have them trade word problems and find their solutions.

3 Assessment

In this lesson students learned to use dot plots and stem-and-leaf plots to interpret data. Use the **Quick Check** problem to assess students' understanding.

Quick Check

To pass a test, the score must be at least a 70. How many students passed the test in Mrs. Wilson's class? 15 students

MAKE A TABLE AND LOOK FOR A PATTERN

Intervention Lesson **J17**

Name ____________________

Make a Table and Look for a Pattern

Intervention Lesson **J17**

Ann and Jane began reading the same book on the same day. If Ann reads 8 pages each day and Jane reads 5 pages each day, what page will Jane read on the day that Ann reads page 40?

Solve by answering 1 to 6.

Answer 1 and 2 to **understand** the problem.

1. What do you know from reading the problem?

   Ann reads __8__ pages each day.

   Jane reads __5__ pages each day.

   They started the same day.

2. What do you need to find?
   What page will Jane read on the day Ann reads page 40?

Answer 3 to 5 to **plan and solve** the problem.

You can solve the problem by making a table and looking for a pattern.

3. Use patterns to complete the table below.

Day	1	2	3	4	5	6
Ann's Page	8	16	24	32	40	48
Jane's Page	5	10	15	20	25	30

4. What day will Ann read page 40? __day 5__
5. What page will Jane read on the day Ann reads page 40? __page 25__

 J17 (student p. 1) MDIS 2.0

Name ____________________

Make a Table and Look for a Pattern (continued)

Intervention Lesson **J17**

Answer 6 to **look back** at your solution.

6. Did you answer the right question? __yes__

Use patterns to complete each table. Solve each problem.

7. Rebecca must put 4 eggs in each basket. There are 8 baskets. How many eggs does she need? __32 eggs__

Number of Baskets	1	2	3	4	5	6	7	8
Number of Eggs	4	8	12	16	20	24	28	32

8. Martin needs to water each tree with 3 gallons of water. How many gallons of water will he need for 7 trees?

Number of trees	1	2	3	4	5	6	7
Gallons of water	3	6	9	12	15	18	21

__Martin will need 21 gallons of water.__

9. Diego recorded the height of a bean plant. The first week, the plant was 2 inches high. The second, third, and fourth week, it was 4 inches, 6 inches, and 8 inches high. At this rate, when will the bean plant be 12 inches high?

Week	1	2	3	4	5	6	7
Height	2	4	6	8	10	12	14

__The bean plant will be 12 inches high in 6 weeks.__

10. Each quilt square has 2 red sections and 3 blue sections. If 18 blue sections are used, how many red sections are needed?

squares	1	2	3	4	5	6
red sections	2	4	6	8	10	12
blue sections	3	6	9	12	15	18

__12 red sections__

 J17 (student p. 2) MDIS 2.0

Objective Students will make a table and look for a pattern.

1 Conceptual Development

Use with Exercises 1–6.

In this lesson you will learn to make a table and look for a pattern.

Have students read the word problem at the top of the page and complete Exercises 1–2. *What page will Jane read on the day that Ann reads page 16?* 10 *What page will Ann read on Day 3?* 24 *What page will Jane read on the day that Ann reads page 24?* 15 Have students continue this pattern to complete the table in Exercise 3 and answer Exercises 4–6.

2 Practice Use with Exercises 7–10.

Encourage students to first read the word problem, think about the information provided and what they need to know, and then use patterns to make a table to solve the problem.

Error Intervention If students have difficulty finding the pattern in the table in Exercise 7, discuss the number of eggs that were added to 4 to get 8. 4 Have them write this number between the 4 and the 8 in the second row of the table and then write it between the 8 and the empty box in column 3. Have them add 8 and 4 and fill in the answer and then write the 4 between the next pair of numbers. Encourage them to use this system as they work through the exercises.

If You Have More Time Have students re-solve Exercise 8 using 6 gallons of water per tree. 42 gallons

3 Assessment

In this lesson students learned to make a table and look for a pattern. Use the **Quick Check** problem to assess students' understanding.

Quick Check  **Formative** Assessment

Re-solve Exercise 9: The first week, the plant was 3 inches high; the second week, it was 6 inches high; and it continued to grow at the same rate. How high was the plant in Week 7? 21 inches

Name ______________________

Intervention Lesson **J18**

Solve a Simpler Problem

Materials color tiles, 10 for each student

Roger is putting up a row of mirror tiles in his entry way, as show at the right. The tiles are squares, 1 foot on each side. How many feet of wood trim does he need to go around 10 tiles in a row?

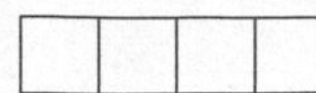

Solve by answering 1 to 6.

Answer 1 and 2 to **understand** the problem.

1. What do you know from reading the problem?

   The tiles are square and each side is __1 foot__ long.

   Roger is putting __10__ tiles in a row.

2. What do you need to find?

   How many feet of trim does Roger need for 10 tiles in a row?

Answer 3 to 5 to **plan and solve** the problem.

You can solve simpler problems, put the solutions in a table, and find a pattern to extend the table in order to solve the problem.

3. Find the feet of trim needed for 3 tiles, 4 tiles, and 5 tiles in a row. You may want to use the picture above. Write the answers in the table below.

Number of tiles	1	2	3	4	5	6	7	8	9	10
Feet of trim	4	6	8	10	12	14	16	18	20	22

4. What is the pattern in the table?

   Each new tile needs 2 more feet of trim.

5. Use the pattern to complete the table. How many feet of wood trim does Roger need to go around 10 tiles in a row? __22 feet__

 J18 (student p. 1) MDIS 2.0

Name ______________________

Intervention Lesson **J18**

Solve a Simpler Problem (continued)

Answer 6 to look back at how you solved the problem.

6. **Reasoning** Was it easier to use simpler problems, a table, and a pattern than it would have been to solve by drawing a picture of 10 tiles in a row? What if there were 50 tiles in a row?

   Answers may vary. Students should see that the approach used in the lesson is easier for larger numbers, even if they don't think it is easier for smaller ones.

Complete each table. Solve each problem.

7. Suppose Mr. Lange had a rope 50 feet long and wanted to cut it into 25 equal pieces. How many cuts would it take?

Pieces	2	3	4	5	6
Cuts	1	2	3	4	5

It would take 24 cuts.

8. The Washington Stars signed up for a single elimination soccer tournament. This means that 2 teams play and the loser is eliminated. There are 8 entries in the tournament. How many games must be played to determine the champion?

Teams	2	3	4	5	6	7	8
Games	1	2	3	4	5	6	7

7 games

9. During the grand opening of a craft store, every fourth customer was given a discount coupon. Every tenth customer was given a discount coupon and a gift. During the grand opening, 120 people visited the store. How many coupons and gifts were given away?

Customers	4	8	10	12	16	20	24	28	30	32	36	40
Gifts	0	0	1	1	1	2	2	2	3	3	3	4
Coupons	1	2	3	4	5	6	7	8	9	10	11	12

12 gifts and 36 coupons

 J18 (student p. 2) MDIS 2.0

Objective Students will solve a simpler problem.
Materials Color tiles, 10 for each student

1 Conceptual Development
Use with Exercises 1–6.

In this lesson you will learn to solve a simpler problem.

Have students read the word problem at the top of the page and look at the tiles. Then have them complete Exercises 1–2. Ask students to look at the table in Exercise 3. *Why is there a 4 under 1 tile?* We are solving a simpler problem, and we know that 1 tile takes 4 feet of trim. *What is the pattern?* The amount of trim increases by 2 feet for each new tile. Have students complete the table in Exercise 3 and then complete Exercises 4–6.

2 Practice **Use with Exercises 7–9.**

Help students see that the strategy of solving a simpler problem, putting the solutions in a table, and then finding a pattern to extend the table makes it easier to solve the original problem, especially when greater numbers are involved.

Error Intervention If students have difficulty finding the patterns in Exercise 9, encourage them to work on each row separately. Have them reread the part of the word problem that discusses the gift and then fill in the Gifts row. Then have them reread the information about coupons and complete the Coupons row of the table. Have students use color tiles as needed.

If You Have More Time Have students write in their own words how the table in Exercise 8 will help them answer the question asked in the problem.

3 Assessment

In this lesson students learned to solve a simpler problem. Use the **Quick Check** problem to assess students' understanding.

Quick Check 

Solve using what you learned in Exercise 7: If Mr. Lange's rope were 100 feet and he wanted to cut the rope into 50 equal pieces, how many cuts would it take? 49 cuts

MAKE A TABLE AND LOOK FOR A PATTERN

Intervention Lesson **J19**

Name ____________________

Make a Table and Look for a Pattern

Intervention Lesson **J19**

Materials 20 unit cubes, for each student

Three fourths of Jamal's CDs are rock and roll. He has 20 or fewer CDs. One way to show $\frac{3}{4}$ is 3 out of 4 equal groups of 5 or $\frac{15}{20}$. Using 20 or fewer cubes, how many other fractions are equivalent to $\frac{3}{4}$?

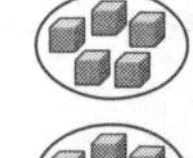
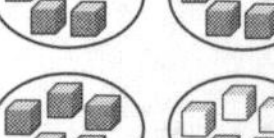

$\frac{15}{20} = \frac{3}{4}$

Solve by answering 1 to 5.

Answer 1 and 2 to **understand** the problem.

1. What do you know from reading the problem?
   Jamal has 20 or fewer CDs. $\frac{3}{4}$ of Jamal's CDs are rock and roll.
2. What do you need to find?
   Using 20 or fewer cubes, how many other fractions are equivalent to $\frac{3}{4}$ besides $\frac{15}{20}$?

Answer 3 and 4 to **plan and solve** the problem.

You can solve the problem by making a table and looking for a pattern.

3. Complete the table. Look for a pattern to help.
4. Using 20 or fewer cubes, how many fractions are equivalent to $\frac{3}{4}$ other than $\frac{15}{20}$? 3

Number of cubes	Cubes in each group	Cubes in 3 groups	Fraction equivalent to $\frac{3}{4}$
20	5	15	$\frac{15}{20}$
16	4	12	$\frac{12}{16}$
12	3	9	$\frac{9}{12}$
8	2	6	$\frac{6}{8}$

Order of rows in the table may vary.

Name ____________________

Make a Table and Look for a Pattern (continued)

Intervention Lesson **J19**

Answer 5 to **look back** at how you solved the problem.

5. **Reasoning** Explain how you know you have all the fractions equivalent to $\frac{3}{4}$, using 20 or fewer cubes.
   Sample answer: With 20 cubes, there are 5 cubes in each group. With only 4 cubes, there is 1 cube in each group and that shows $\frac{3}{4}$. Between 1 and 5, it is possible to have 2, 3, and 4 cubes in each group. So, there are 3 other fractions.

Complete each table. Solve each problem.

6. You are making a bulletin board display of 21 drawings. If you put them in a triangular pattern, how many rows will the drawings make?

Row	1	2	3	4	5	6
Drawings in the Row	1	2	3	4	5	6
Total Drawings Used	1	3	6	10	15	21

The drawings will make 6 rows.

7. Each box lunch has 3 cookies and 4 baby carrots. If 15 cookies are used to make some box lunches, how many baby carrots are used?

Lunch Boxes	1	2	3	4	5	6
Cookies	3	6	9	12	15	18
Baby Carrots	4	8	12	16	20	24

20 baby carrots are used.

8. Suppose you divide a rectangle with 10 straight lines. What is the greatest number of sections you can form?

1 line, 2 pieces
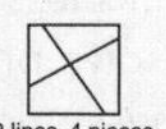
2 lines, 4 pieces
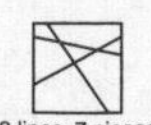
3 lines, 7 pieces

Lines	1	2	3	4	5	6	7	8	9	10
Pieces	1	4	7	11	16	22	29	37	46	56

56 is the greatest number of pieces.

Objective Students will make a table and look for a pattern.
Vocabulary Pattern, table
Materials 20 unit cubes for each student

1 Conceptual Development

Use with Exercises 1–5.

In this lesson you will learn to make a table and look for a pattern.

Revisit the terms *pattern* and *table*. Have students read the word problem and look at the picture. *Why are the groups circled?* They are divided into fourths. *Why are three of the groups shaded?* To show three-fourths Have students complete Exercises 1–2 and use the unit cubes to create even groups of 4. *What is another group of cubes we can divide evenly into 4 groups?* 16 *Why won't 19 or 18 work?* Because 4 does not divide evenly into them Have students use the cubes to complete Exercises 3–5.

2 Practice Use with Exercises 6–8.

Encourage students to use the cubes, as needed, to help them solve a problem by making a table and looking for a pattern.

Error Intervention If students have difficulty creating an image of the display in Exercise 6, draw it on the board and encourage them to use cubes to make Row 1, using one drawing (cube) for the top. Then have them add a second row, reminding them that they are making a triangle. As each row is added, have students write down what they did by counting the cubes in the row and the total cubes.

If You Have More Time Have students continue the table in Exercise 7, finding how many cookies and carrots would be used for 10 lunch boxes. 30 cookies and 40 carrots

3 Assessment

In this lesson students learned to make a table and look for a pattern. Use the **Quick Check** problem to assess students' understanding.

Quick Check

Draw a table and solve: Each ball player gets 3 shirts and 2 caps at the start of the season. If there are 12 players, how many shirts and caps are needed? 36 shirts and 24 caps

Intervention Lesson **J20**

Name ______________________

Intervention Lesson J20

Analyze Relationships

Andrea spent \$4.25 on wooden sticks and \$1.75 on glue to make birdhouses. She sold 3 birdhouses for \$2.50 each. How much profit did Andrea make?

Answer 1 and 2 to **understand** the problem.

1. What do you know from reading the problem?

   Andrea spent \$4.25 on wooden sticks.

   Andrea spent \$1.75 on glue.

   Andrea sold 3 birdhouses.

   Andrea sold each birdhouse for \$2.50.

2. What do you need to find?
   How much profit Andrea made

Answer 3 to 5 to **plan and solve** the problem.

3. How can you find the total cost of the materials used to make the birdhouses?
   Sample answer: Add the cost of the materials, so $\$4.25 + \$1.75 = \$6.00$

4. How can you find the amount of money Andrea received for selling the 3 birdhouses?
   Sample answer: Multiply the price of a birdhouse by the number of birdhouses sold, so $\$2.50 \times 3 = \$7.50$

5. How much profit did Andrea make? Use your answers to 3 and 4 to solve.
   Sample answer: $\$7.50 - \$6.00 = \$1.50$; Andrea made a profit of \$1.50.

Name ______________________

Intervention Lesson J20

Analyze Relationships (continued)

Answer 6 to **look back** at how you solved the problem.

6. Explain how you used the total amount of money Andrea spent and received to find how much profit she made.
   Sample answer: I subtracted the cost of the materials from the amount of money that Andrea received for selling the birdhouses.

Solve each problem.

7. Luis spends \$7.50 on supplies. He makes and sells 3 items for \$5.00 each. What is his profit?
   Sample answer: $\$5.00 \times 3 = \$15.00$ and $15.00 - \$7.50 = \$7.50$; So, Luis makes a profit of \$7.50.

8. Beth spends \$3.50 on supplies. She makes and sells 4 items for \$2.25 each. What is her profit?
   Sample answer: $\$2.25 \times 4 = \$9.00$ and $\$9.00 - \$3.50 = \$5.50$; So, Beth makes a profit of \$5.50.

Use the table at the right to answer 9 to 11.

	Jennifer	Michelle
Money Spent	\$8.25	\$6.85
Money Received	\$13.40	\$12.35

9. How much is Jennifer's profit?
   $\$13.40 - \$8.25 = \$5.15$

10. How much is Michelle's profit?
    $\$12.35 - \$6.85 = \$5.50$

11. **Reasoning** Did Jennifer or Michelle make the greater profit? Explain.
    Michelle; Sample answer: $\$5.50 > \$5.15$

Objective Students will analyze relationships to solve problems.
Vocabulary Profit

1 Conceptual Development
Use with Exercises 1–6.

In this lesson you will learn to analyze relationships to solve problems.

Have students read the problem and analyze it by completing Exercises 1–2. Remind students that profit is the amount of money you make after subtracting what you spent. Students should continue to plan and solve the problem. *Why do you need to plan your solution before you solve a problem?* Sample answer: So that I do not do a lot of unnecessary or unhelpful steps Have students complete Exercises 3–5. *What is the relationship between the answers to Exercises 3–4 and Exercise 5?* To find the profit in Exercise 5, you have to subtract the answer to Exercise 3 from the answer to Exercise 4. *Why is looking back important after you solve the problem?* Sample answer: To make sure I did it correctly Have students complete Exercise 6.

2 Practice **Use with Exercises 7–11.**

Remind students that when solving problems, they should follow each step: understand, plan, solve, and look back.

Error Intervention If students have difficulty finding profits from the table, remind them that profit is equal to money received minus money spent. For example, Jennifer's profit would be $\$13.40 - \$8.25 = \$5.15$.

If You Have More Time Have students set up their own shops, identifying their costs and how much they will sell things for. Then have them determine what they sell and what their profit is. Record the class's information in a table like the one shown.

3 Assessment

In this lesson students learned to analyze relationships to solve problems. Use the **Quick Check** problem to assess students' understanding.

Quick Check 

Miguel spends \$11.20 on supplies. He then sells 6 packages for \$7.00 each. What is his profit? \$30.80

Name ______________________

Use Objects

Intervention Lesson **J21**

Materials color tiles, 16 for each student

Jada bought balloons for the party. She bought red, yellow, and blue balloons. She bought at least one of each color. Use the information at the right to find how many balloons of each color she bought.

Balloons Jada Bought
7 yellow 3 more red than blue 16 balloons in all

Solve by answering 1 to 6.

Answer 1 to 3 to **understand** the problem.

1. What do you know from reading the problem?
   Jada bought __red__, __yellow__, and __blue__ balloons.
2. What do you know from reading the chart?
   Jada bought __7__ yellow balloons.
   Jada bought __3__ more red balloons than blue balloons.
   Jada bought __16__ balloons in all.
3. What do you need to find?
   How many balloons of each color did Jada buy?

Answer 4 and 5 to **plan and solve** the problem.

You can solve the problem by acting out the problem with color tiles.

4. Count out 16 tiles. Separate 7 of them for the yellow balloons. How many red and blue balloons did Jada buy? __9__

 J21 (student p. 1) MDIS 2.0

Name ______________________

Use Objects (continued)

Intervention Lesson **J21**

5. Separate the tiles representing the red and blue balloons into two piles, so one pile has 3 more tiles than the other. How many balloons of each color did Jada buy?
   __7__ yellow __6__ red __3__ blue

Answer 6 to **check** your solution.

6. **Reasoning** Explain why your answer is correct.
   Sample answer: $7 + 6 + 3 = 16$ and 6 is 3 more than 3.

Solve each problem.

7. Min is playing with modeling clay. To try to protect the table, his mother put down a plastic placemat. The placemat had 40 small squares on it. How many squares were in each row?
   __8 squares__

8. There are 17 entries in the photo contest. The photos consist of animal photos, nature photos, and portraits. There are 5 portraits. There are 6 fewer nature photos than animal photos. How many of each type of photo was in the contest?
   __5 portraits, 3 nature, 9 animal__
9. Tim bought 18 apples for the apple-bobbing contest. He bought red, yellow, and green apples. There are 3 yellow apples. There are twice as many red apples as green apples. How many of each color apple did he buy?
   __3 yellow, 5 green, 10 red__

 J21 (student p. 2) MDIS 2.0

Objective Students will use objects to solve problems.
Materials Color tiles, 16 for each student

1 Conceptual Development

Use with Exercises 1–6.

In this lesson you will learn to use objects to solve problems.

Have students read the word problem and look at the box containing the information. Then have students complete Exercises 1–3 and read Exercise 4. *Why are we counting out 16 tiles?* Jada had 16 balloons in all. Have students separate the 7 tiles and subtract to find how many red and blue balloons she bought. Then have students follow the steps in Exercise 5 to determine how many balloons of each color Jada bought. Have students complete Exercise 6.

2 Practice **Use with Exercises 7–9.**

Remind students to think about what they know from the problem and what they need to find before solving.

Error Intervention If students have difficulty solving Exercise 7, have them work in groups of 3 and combine tiles. Have group members tell what they know from reading the problem and what they have to find out. Then have them separate the tiles to find the answer.

If You Have More Time Have students find another solution to Exercise 7. 10 rows with 4 small squares in each row

3 Assessment

In this lesson students learned to use objects to solve problems. Use the **Quick Check** problem to assess students' understanding.

Quick Check

Nicky has 14 pencils. There are 2 yellow pencils and twice as many green pencils as blue ones. How many blue pencils and green pencils does Nicky have?
4 blue pencils and 8 green pencils

Name ____________________

Use Objects

Intervention Lesson **J22**

Materials color tiles, 6 for each student, crayons, markers, or colored pencils

A hexomino is an arrangement of 6 identical squares that are attached to one another edge to edge. Find 4 different hexominoes, that have 4 squares in a row.

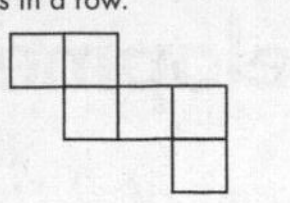

This is a hexomino.

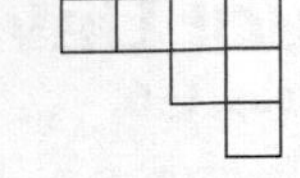

This is not a hexomino.

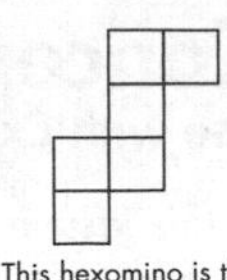

This hexomino is the same as the first one.

Solve by answering 1 to 5.

Answer 1 and 2 to **understand** the problem.

1. What do you know from reading the problem?

A hexomino has __6__ identical squares that are attached to one another edge to edge

2. What do you need to find?

Find 4 different hexominoes, that have 4 squares in a row.

Answer 3 and 4 to **plan and solve** the problem.

You can solve the problem by using objects.

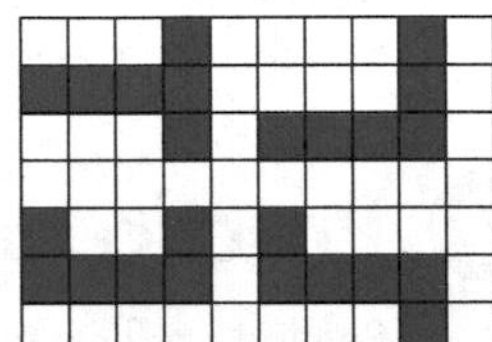

3. Put 4 tiles in a row. Add the other two tiles to make a hexomino. Color the grid at the right to show the hexomino you found.

4. Change the tiles to find 3 more hexominos with 4 squares in a row. Color the grid to show each one.

 J22 (student p. 1) MDIS 2.0

Name ____________________

Use Objects (continued)

Intervention Lesson **J22**

Answer 5 to **look back** at how you solved the problem.

5. Did the color tiles help you solve the problem? __yes__

Solve each problem.

6. Find 4 hexominoes with no more than 3 squares in a row. Show your hexominoes by coloring the grid at the right. Sample answers are shown.

7. A board is divided into four sections. Two sections will be painted gray and two sections will be painted white. How many different patterns are possible?

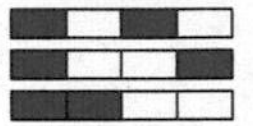
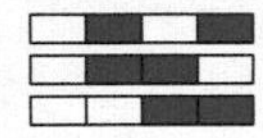

6 patterns

8. Six children form a triangle. How can they turn the triangle upside down if only two of the children move? Draw two arrows on the picture to show your answer.

9. Ten children form a triangle. How can they turn the triangle upside down if only three of the children move? Draw three arrows on the diagram at the right to show your answer.

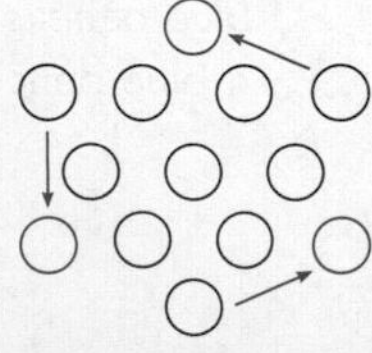

 J22 (student p. 2) MDIS 2.0

Objective Students will use objects to solve problems.
Vocabulary Hexomino
Materials Color tiles, 6 for each student; crayons, markers, or colored pencils

1 Conceptual Development
Use with Exercises 1–5.

In this lesson you will learn to use objects to solve problems.

Revisit the term *hexomino* as needed. Have students read the sentences at the top of the page. *Why is the first picture a hexomino?* It has 6 identical squares attached to each other edge to edge. *Why isn't the second picture a hexomino?* All of the squares' edges are not attached. Have students complete Exercises 1–2 and then use their tiles to complete Exercises 3–5.

2 Practice Use with Exercises 6–9.

Encourage students to draw a picture or use objects, such as color tiles, to help them solve each exercise.

Error Intervention If students have difficulty seeing the images in Exercise 8, have six students form a triangle sitting on the floor. Then have two children move to turn the triangle upside down. Have students recreate that image with their tiles and then add arrows to the exercise to solve.

If You Have More Time Have students write a description, using only words, to tell how they solved Exercise 9.

3 Assessment

In this lesson students learned to use objects to solve problems. Use the **Quick Check** problem to assess students' understanding.

Quick Check

Formative Assessment

Use six tiles to create a hexomino, show a pattern that is not a hexomino, and then tell the characteristics of each. Check students' tile arrangements. A hexomino has 6 identical squares that are attached to one another edge to edge.

Intervention Lesson J23

Name ______________________

Use Reasoning

Materials color tiles, 15 for each student

Laurel has 15 cousins who live in three different states. Three of the cousins live in Montana. Twice as many cousins live in Indiana as live in Wisconsin. How many cousins live in each state?

Solve by answering 1 to 5.

Answer 1 and 2 to **understand** the problem.

1. What do you know from reading the problem?

   Laurel has __15__ cousins.

   Three of Laurel's cousins live in __Montana__.

   __2__ times as many cousins live in Indiana as live in Wisconsin.

2. What do you need to find?

   How many of Laurel's cousins live in each state?

Answer 3 and 4 to **plan and solve** the problem.

You can solve the problem by using objects and reasoning.

3. Count out 15 tiles. Separate 3 of them for the cousins who live in Montana. How many cousins live in Indiana and Wisconsin combined? __12__

4. Separate the tiles representing the cousins who live in Indiana and Wisconsin, so one pile has twice as many tiles as the other. How many of Laurel's cousins live in each state?

   __3__ in Montana __8__ in Indiana __4__ in Wisconsin

Answer 5 to **look back** at how you solved the problem.

5. **Reasoning** Explain why your answer is correct.

   Sample answer: $3 + 8 + 4 = 15$ and 8 is twice 4.

 J23 (student p. 1) MDIS 2.0

Name ______________________

Intervention Lesson J23

Use Reasoning (continued)

Solve each problem.

6. Mr. Parvey spilled some cement paint on his patio. Since he was going to paint the patio in a checker board pattern, it was marked in 54 square sections. How many sections were in each row?

   __9 sections__

7. Wanda carries a stack of 17 books. Lyle carries a stack of 11 books. How many books should Wanda give Lyle so they carry the same number? __3 books__

8. Bill, Phillip, and Mandy each have 7 baseball cards. Suppose Bill gives 3 of his to Phillip, and Phillip gives 2 of his to Mandy. How many cards does Phillip have? __8__

9. A sporting goods store would like to display a new line of tennis balls in a triangular stack. The bottom row will have 7 canisters and each row going up will have one less canister. How many canisters will be on display? __28__

10. The Harris children collect snow globes. Jill has 5, Brad has 7, and Tracey has 6, but 3 of hers broke when the family moved. If Mrs. Harris asks the children to share the snow globes equally, how many will each child get? __5__

11. Andrew folds a sheet of paper in half 5 times. When he opens it up, how many sections will there be? __32__

12. The perimeter of a rectangular poster is 120 inches. The length of the poster is three times its width. What are the dimensions of the length of the poster?

    __length = 45 in., width = 15 in.__

 J23 (student p. 2) MDIS 2.0

Objective Students will use reasoning to solve problems.
Vocabulary Reasoning
Materials Color tiles, 15 for each student

1 Conceptual Development
Use with Exercises 1–5.

In this lesson you will learn to use reasoning to solve problems.

Discuss the term *reasoning*. Guide students to understand that reasoning refers to using logic or having reasons for what you do or think. Have students read the word problem at the top of the page and then use the information to complete Exercises 1–2. *How many tiles would we start with to solve this problem?* 15 Have students follow the steps in Exercises 3–5.

2 Practice **Use with Exercises 6–12.**

Remind students that they can solve some problems by using objects and reasoning. Encourage them to first identify the total in the problem and what they need to know as they begin to solve.

Error Intervention If students have difficulty using reasoning to solve the problems, have them work with a partner and combine their tiles. Then have them read to find the total and count out those tiles. Have students read the rest of the problem to find what they will do with their pile of tiles. After students solve, have them draw a picture to the side of the word problem to show what they did.

If You Have More Time Have students create an equation to show what they did for Exercise 10. $5 + 7 + (6 - 3) \div 3 = 15 \div 3 = 5$

3 Assessment

In this lesson students learned to use reasoning to solve problems. Use the **Quick Check** problem to assess students' understanding.

Quick Check Formative Assessment

Marty and his friends want to pool their money and divide it equally to buy lunch. 2 of his friends have \$3 and one has \$4. Marty has \$2. How much money will each of the 4 boys have for lunch? \$3

Objective Students will use reasoning to solve problems.
Vocabulary Reasoning
Materials Place-value blocks, 36 unit cubes for each student

1 Conceptual Development

Use with Exercises 1–7.

In this lesson you will learn to use reasoning to solve problems.

Remind students that using reasoning to solve a problem means "using logic and having an explanation for the solution." Have students read the word problem at the top of the page and look at the picture. *How many boxes does Mandy's dad have to stack?* 36 *Are all of the boxes the same size and shape?* Yes *How many stickers does Mandy's dad have to use?* 66 Encourage students to think through the problem step-by-step as they complete Exercises 1–7.

2 Practice Use with Exercises 8–11.

Explain to students that, when cutting something into equal-sized pieces, it takes one less cut than the number of equal pieces needed. They can use this information to more easily answer Exercises 10–11.

Error Intervention

If students have difficulty using reasoning to solve a problem, have them work with a partner and use a checklist to work through the following steps: *What do we know? What do we need to find? How many cubes will we start with? What do we do first?*

If You Have More Time

Have students write in words the strategy they used to solve Exercise 10.

3 Assessment

In this lesson students learned to use reasoning to solve problems. Use the **Quick Check** problem to assess students' understanding.

Quick Check

Formative Assessment

Molly has a circle cake with a radius of 6 inches and a square cake with a side length of 1 foot. How can she use these two cakes to make a heart-shaped cake? Cut the circle cake in half and place each half along consecutive sides of the square

---

Name ______________________

Intervention Lesson **J24**

Use Reasoning

Materials place-value blocks, 36 units cubes for each student

Mandy's dad has to stack 36 boxes, in the shape of a rectangular prism, for shipping. All the boxes are the same size cube. He needs to put a sticker on each side of a box that is on the outside when they are stacked, including the bottom. He has 66 stickers. How can he stack the boxes so he has enough stickers?

Solve by answering 1 to 7.

Answer 1 and 2 to **understand** the problem.

1. What do you know from reading the problem?

   Mandy's dad has to stack __36__ boxes that are all the same size __cube__.

   Mandy's dad has __66__ stickers and has to put one on each side of a box that is on the outside when the boxes are stacked.

2. What do you need to find?
   How can Mandy's dad stack the boxes so he has enough stickers?

Answer 3 to 6 to **plan and solve** the problem.

You can solve by using objects and reasoning.

3. Stack 36 cubes to form a 6 by 2 by 3 rectangular prism. How many sides of a small cube are on the outside of the stack? __72 sides__

4. Is the number of sides greater than or less than 66? __greater than__

5. Change the shape of the stack until you get a rectangular prism with 66 or fewer sides on the outside of the stack. What are the dimensions of the prism? __3__ by __3__ by __4__

6. How can Mandy's dad stack the boxes so he has enough stickers?
   Sample answer: He can put 3 by 3 boxes in each layer and stack them 4 layers high.

Name ______________________

Intervention Lesson **J24**

Use Reasoning (continued)

Answer 7 to **look back** at how you solved the problem?

7. **Reasoning** How did objects help you solve the problem.
   Sample answer: By stacking the cubes, it was easier to find the number of outside sides.

Solve each problem. Use objects and reasoning.

8. Mandy's dad stacks 36 boxes, in a 3 by 3 by 4 rectangular prism, for shipping. All the boxes are the same size cube. He put a sticker on each side of a box that is on the outside when they are stacked. How many of the small boxes have stickers on 3 sides? On 2 sides? On 1 side? On no sides?

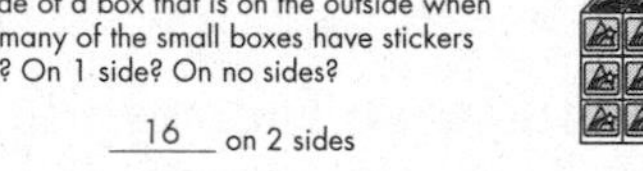

   __8__ on 3 sides   __16__ on 2 sides
   __10__ on 1 side   __2__ on no sides

9. David wants to make a flower garden by enclosing it with landscape timbers. If a landscape timber is 8 feet long, and he has 6 timbers, what is the maximum area of garden space he can enclose?
   __8 by 16 = 128 square feet__

10. How can you cut a double-layer cake into 8 pieces with only 3 straight cuts? Hint: Use two pieces of paper to represent the two layers of the cake.
    Cut two diagonals across the cake and make a third cut that separates the two layers.

11. Mr. Lange cut a 25-foot rope into 12 equal-sized pieces. How many cuts did he make?
    There is 1 less cut than the number of equal pieces needed. It will take Mr. Lange 11 cuts to make 12 equal-size pieces.

Name ____________

Draw a Picture

Intervention Lesson J25

Braxton is making a diagram of the distance between his house and his grandmother's house. He lives 0.9 mile from his grandmother. He knows the store is 0.2 miles from his house and has it marked on the diagram below. Where should Braxton's grandmother's house be placed on the diagram?

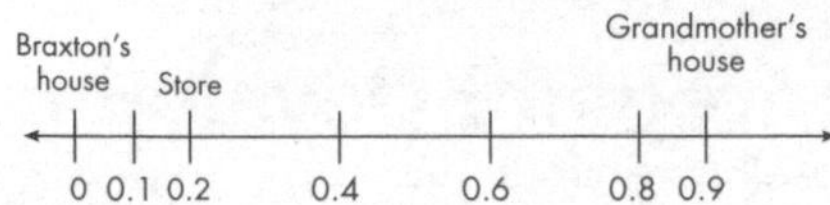

Solve by answering 1 to 6.

Answer 1 and 2 to **understand** the problem.

1. What do you know from reading the problem?

   Braxton lives 0.9 mile from his grandmother.

   The store is 0.2 mile from Braxton's house.

2. What do you need to find?
   Where should Braxton's grandmother's house by placed on the diagram?

Answer 3 to 5 to **plan and solve** the problem.

You can solve by drawing a picture.

3. Mark the distance from 0 to 0.2 on a piece of paper. Then, use the marks to mark the distance 0.2 mile more from Braxton's house on the diagram. How far is this from Braxton's house? 0.4 mile

 J25 (student p. 1) MDIS 2.0

Name ____________

Draw a Picture (continued)

Intervention Lesson J25

4. Mark and label this distance two more times.

5. Half of the distance between Braxton's house and the store is 0.1 mile. Mark 0.1 mile from Braxton's house on the diagram above. Use the distance from 0 to 0.1 to finish marking the distance to Grandmother's house in the diagram.

Answer 6 to **look back** at how you solved the problem.

6. Did you solve the right problem? yes

Solve each problem.

7. Alicia is making a diagram of the distance between her house and school. She lives 0.9 mile from school. She knows the park is 0.6 miles from her house and has it marked on the diagram below. Where should Alicia's school be placed on the diagram?

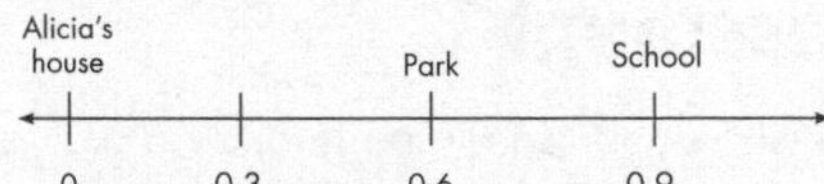

8. A helicopter is 150 feet above sea level. A submarine is directly below it, 100 feet below sea level. What is the distance between the helicopter and the submarine? 250 feet

9. You are planting pepper plants in a garden. Your garden is only 48 inches long. The plants must be planted 6 inches apart and the first and last plant must be 6 inches from the edge of the garden. How many plants can you plant in a row?

   You can plant 7 plants in a row.

10. You are in a town with square blocks. You walk 5 blocks east, 3 blocks north, then 2 blocks west. How many blocks do you need to walk to get back to your starting point?

    You need to walk 6 blocks.

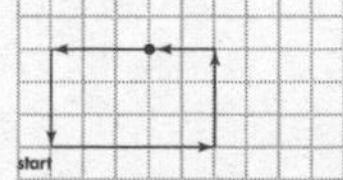

 J25 (student p. 2) MDIS 2.0

Objective Students will draw a picture to solve a problem.
Vocabulary Diagram

1 Conceptual Development

Use with Exercises 1–6.

In this lesson you will learn to draw a picture to solve a problem.

Have students read the word problem at the top of the page and then look at the diagram. Explain that a diagram is a type of picture or drawing. *What does this diagram show?* The distance from the house to the store *Where did the numbers come from?* The values are in the word problem. Have students complete Exercises 1–2 and discuss before reading the steps and completing Exercises 3–6.

2 Practice Use with Exercises 7–10.

Remind students that the more accurate the drawing, the more likely they are to understand the problem. Encourage students to label their drawings with information from the problem to help guide their problem solving.

Error Intervention If students have difficulty solving Exercise 8, draw a line and tell students that it is the sea. Write *above* and *below* and discuss how, in this problem, *above sea level* is in the air, and *below sea level* is in the water. Have students add the measures to the diagram and solve.

If You Have More Time Have students solve the following problem: *Jack walks 0.5 mile to Mike's house, back home to get his ball cap, and then back to Mike's house. The boys then walk 0.3 miles to the ball field. How far has Jack walked?* 0.5 + 0.5 + 0.5 + 0.3 = 1.8 miles

3 Assessment

In this lesson students learned to draw a picture to solve a problem. Use the **Quick Check** problem to assess students' understanding.

Quick Check  **Formative** Assessment

Using the information in Exercise 7, figure out the distance from the park to the school. If Alicia walked from her home to the park to the school, would she have walked a mile? No, she would have walked 0.9 mile.

Name ______________________

Draw a Picture

Intervention Lesson **J26**

Katie has only white and blue socks. The ratio of white socks to blue socks is 5 to 6. What fraction of Katie's socks are blue?

Solve by answering 1 to 5.

Answer 1 and 2 to **understand** the problem.

1. What do you know from reading the problem?

   Katie has only white and blue socks.

   The ratio of Katie's white socks to her blue socks is 5 to 6.

2. What do you need to find?

   What fraction of Katie's socks are blue?

Answer 3 and 4 to **plan and solve** the problem.

You can solve by drawing a picture.

3. Draw a picture of Katie's socks so the ratio of white socks to blue socks is 5 to 6.
   Students should draw 5 white and 6 blue socks. They could also draw 10 white and 12 blue or any equivalent ratio.

4. What fraction of Katie's socks are blue? $\frac{6}{11}$

Answer 5 to **look back at and extend** the problem.

5. **Reasoning** How did a picture help you solve the problem?
   Sample answer: The picture showed that $\frac{6}{11}$ of the socks were blue, when it seemed that $\frac{5}{6}$ or $\frac{6}{5}$ were blue without the picture.

6. If the ratio of white socks to blue socks was 8 to 10, what fraction of Katie's socks would be blue? Write the fraction in simplest form.
   $\frac{10}{18} = \frac{5}{9}$

Name ______________________

Draw a Picture (continued)

Intervention Lesson **J26**

Solve each problem by drawing or completing the picture provided.

7. At lunch, Sara and Jim are third and fourth in line. There are 7 people behind them. How many people are in line?
   There are 11 people in line.

8. A roller coaster has a train of 5 cars that are each 6 feet long. The cars are 2 feet apart. How long is the train?

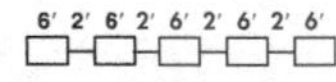

   The train is 38 feet long.

9. A square garden is 10 feet long. A square walkway 3 feet wide goes all the way around the garden. How many feet of fence is needed to go around the walkway?

   64 feet of fence is needed.

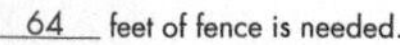

10. Two-thirds of the area of a farm is planted with wheat. The wheat covers 4 acres. What is the area of the farm?
    The area of the farm is 6 acres.

11. A straight fence is 24 feet long. There is a fence post every 6 feet. How many posts are there in the fence?
    5 posts

12. When a ball bounces, it returns to $\frac{1}{2}$ of its previous height. If Ken drops a ball from 20 feet, how many feet will it have traveled when it hits the ground the second time?
    The ball will travel 40 feet.

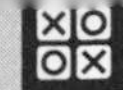

Objective Students will draw a picture to solve a problem.
Vocabulary Ratio

1 Conceptual Development
Use with Exercises 1–6.

In this lesson you will learn to draw a picture to solve a problem.

Revisit the term *ratio* as needed. Have students read the word problem at the top of the page and complete Exercises 1–2. Model how to draw a picture of the ratio of white socks to blue socks. *If we write this ratio in a fraction, which number is the denominator, or the number on the bottom?* 6 *Which number is the numerator, or the number on the top?* 5 Have students complete Exercises 3–6.

2 Practice Use with Exercises 7–12.

Remind students to think about what they know from the problem and what they are asked to find. Tell them that drawing a picture can help them solve the problem.

Error Intervention If students have difficulty solving Exercise 7, have students line up and ask the third and fourth students in line to be Sara and Jim. Have students count aloud 7 more students after Jim to find the end of the line. Then have students count aloud from the beginning of the line to the end of the line to see how many students are in line altogether.

If You Have More Time Have students re-solve Exercise 8 with a train of 5 cars, each 7 feet long and 3 feet apart. The train is 47 feet long.

3 Assessment

In this lesson students learned to draw a picture to solve a problem. Use the **Quick Check** problem to assess students' understanding.

A child's block fence is 18 inches long. Blocks making up the fence are each 3 inches long with 2 inches between each one. How many blocks are in the block fence? 4 blocks

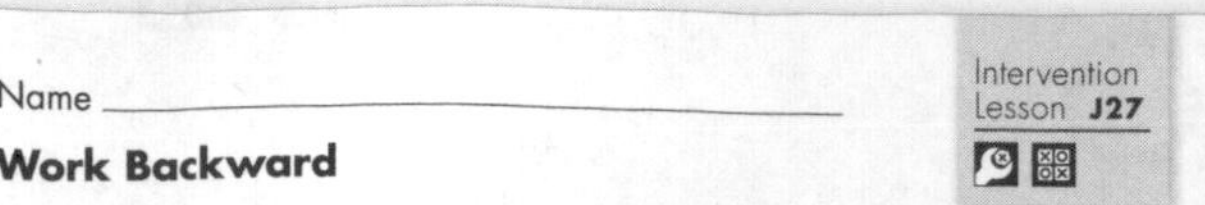

Name ____________

Work Backward

Intervention Lesson J27

Between 4:00 P.M. and 5:00 P.M., the temperature dropped 4 degrees. Every hour after that, the temperature dropped 2 degrees. At 8:00 P.M., the temperature was 52°F. What was the temperature at 4:00 P.M.?

F 70 60 50 40

8:00 P.M.

Solve by answering 1 to 7.

Answer 1 and 2 to **understand** the problem.

1. What do you know from reading the problem?

   The temperature dropped __4__ degrees, between 4:00 P.M. and 5:00 P.M.

   The temperature dropped __2__ degrees, every hour after 5:00 P.M.

   The temperature was __52°F__ at 8:00 P.M.

2. What do you need to find?

   __What was the temperature at 4:00 P.M.?__

Answer 3 to 5 to **plan and solve** the problem.

You can solve by working backward.

3. The temperature dropped 2 degrees from 7:00 P.M. to 8:00 P.M. The temperature was 52°F at 8:00 p.m. What was the temperature at 7:00 P.M.? Write your answer in the diagram below.

4:00 P.M.	5:00 P.M.	6:00 P.M.	7:00 P.M.	8:00 P.M.
−4 →	−2 →	−2 →	−2 →	
62°F	58°F	56°F	54°F	52°F
← +4	← +2	← +2	← +2	

Name ____________

Work Backward (continued)

Intervention Lesson J27

4. Find the temperature at 6:00 P.M., then 5:00 P.M., then 4:00 P.M. Write each in the diagram on the previous page.

5. What was the temperature at 4:00 P.M.? __62°F__

Answer 6 and 7 to **look back and check** your solution to the problem.

6. The temperature dropped 2 degrees from 7:00 P.M. to 8:00 P.M., which means you subtract 2. When working backward from 8:00 P.M. to 7:00 P.M., do you add or subtract 2? __add__

7. If the temperature was the one you found at 4:00 P.M. and changed as described in the problem, would it be 52°F at 8:00 P.M.? __yes__

Solve each problem.

8. It takes Josh 10 minutes to get ready for soccer practice and 25 minutes to bike to the field. He needs to eat a snack before he gets ready and that takes 15 minutes. Soccer practice is at 4:30. What time does Josh need to start eating his snack to get to soccer practice on time? __3:40__

9. Lola took 45 minutes to get ready for school. She walked to school in 20 minutes and then waited 5 minutes before the bell rang at 8:55 A.M. What time did she get out of bed that morning?

   __7:45 A.M.__

10. The trip from your home to the museum takes 45 minutes. You need 1 hour and 30 minutes to tour a special exhibit in the museum. You want to finish the tour before 3:00 P.M. What is the latest time you should leave home to go to the museum?

    __12:45 P.M.__

Objective Students will work backward to solve problems.

1 Conceptual Development

Use with Exercises 1–7.

In this lesson you will learn to work backward to solve problems.

Read the problem aloud with students. Have students complete Exercises 1–2. *What do you know from the problem?* We know that the temperature dropped 4° between 4:00 P.M. and 5:00 P.M. and that every hour between 5:00 P.M. and 8:00 P.M., it dropped 2°. We also know that the temperature was 52°F at 8:00 P.M. *What do you need to find?* The temperature at 4:00 P.M. Explain that since you know the end temperature and how many degrees it changed per hour, you can work backward to find the start temperature. *The temperature dropped 2° between 7:00 P.M. and 8:00 P.M. What can you do to work backward to find the temperature at 7:00 P.M.?* Add 2° to 52°F to get 54°F at 7:00 P.M. *What would the temperature be at 6:00 P.M.?* 56°F Have students complete Exercises 3–7.

2 Practice **Use with Exercises 8–10.**

Remind students that, at times, the best way to find the solution to a problem is to work backward to find the answer.

Error Intervention If students have difficulty working backward to solve a problem, have them highlight the information they know so they can use it to work backward to solve the problem.

If You Have More Time Have students take their answers and work forward to see whether they get the number they started with.

3 Assessment

In this lesson students learned to work backward to solve problems. Use the **Quick Check** problem to assess students' understanding.

Quick Check  Formative Assessment

Work backward to solve: Joe walked from his house to the park. An hour and 25 minutes passed, and he left the park and went to the mall. He was at the mall for 50 minutes and left at 8:15 P.M. What time did Joe leave his house? 6:00 P.M.

Name ____________________

Intervention
Lesson **J28**

Work Backward

Jean cuts 30 inches off a board to make a shelf. Then she cuts the rest of the board into 4 equal pieces. Each piece is 6 inches long. How long was the original board?

Solve by answering 1 to 5.

Answer 1 and 2 to **understand** the problem.

1. What do you know from reading the problem?

Jean cuts <u>30</u> inches off a board to make a shelf.

Then, Jean cuts the board into <u>4</u> equal pieces.

Each of the equal pieces is <u>6</u> inches long.

2. What do you need to find?

<u>How long was the original board?</u>

Answer 3 and 4 to **plan and solve** the problem.

You can solve by working backward.

3. Jean cut the board into 4 equal pieces and each piece was 6 inches long. How long was the board before Jean cut it into 4 equal parts? Write your answer in the diagram below.

Original board		
−30 →	÷ 4 →	
54	24	6
← +30	← ×4	

4. How long was the board before Jean cut off 30 inches, that is, how long was the original board? <u>54 inches</u>

Name ____________________

Intervention
Lesson **J28**

Work Backward (continued)

Answer 5 to **look back at and extend** the problem.

5. Reasoning Jean cut off 30 inches, which means she subtracted 30 inches from the length of the board. When working backward, do you add or subtract 30? <u>add</u>

Solve each problem by working backward.

6. Jeb bought a CD for $14.99 plus $1.19 for tax. He had $3.82 left. How much money did he have before he bought the CD? <u>$20</u>

7. There were 7 people on a bus. At the next stop, 4 women got on and 4 men got off the bus. Of the 7 people on the bus, $\frac{4}{7}$ were women. How many women were on the bus to start? <u>none</u>

8. A store reduced the price of a DVD player by $15. A week later, all prices in the store were cut in half for a clearance sale. The clearance price of the DVD player was $47. What was the original price? <u>$109</u>

9. Ana spent half her savings on a pair of skates. Then she spent $12 on a CD. If she earned $5 and now has $65, how much money did she have before she bought the skates? <u>$144</u>

Solve each problem. Use any strategy.

10. Charlotte bowled 3 games. Her average score was 142. What was her total for the 3 games together?

average score = total score ÷ number of games
$142 = T \div 3$
$142 \times 3 = (T \div 3) \times 3$
$426 = T$

<u>426</u>

11. Two families went bowling. They paid for 4 adult games and 4 bumper bowling games, but no one rented shoes. What was the total cost they paid?

Bowling Prices (per game)	
Adults	$3.35
Bumper bowling	$3.70
Shoe rental (per person)	$2.00

4 adult games = $13.40
4 bumper games = $14.80, Total = $28.20

Objective Students will work backward to solve problems.

1 Conceptual Development
Use with Exercises 1–5.

In this lesson you will learn to work backward to solve problems.

Have students read the problem and complete Exercises 1–2. *What do you know from the problem?* There are 4 pieces of board that are each 6 inches long and one piece that is 30 inches. *What do you need to find out?* The length of the board originally Since you know the measurements of all of the smaller pieces of wood, how can you work backward to find the length of the original board? Multiply the small pieces and then add the product to the 30-inch piece Have students complete Exercises 3–5.

2 Practice **Use with Exercises 6–11.**

Remind students to take the information they know and make a plan to use this information to work backward to find the solution.

Error Intervention If students have difficulty working backward to solve a problem, have them circle the information in the problem that will help them solve the problem. Then have them use that information to make a plan to work backward.

If You Have More Time Have students write a problem that requires a partner to work backward to find the solution.

3 Assessment

In this lesson students learned to work backward to solve problems. Use the **Quick Check** problem to assess students' understanding.

Quick Check

Work backward to solve: David filled the gas tank in his car before starting his week. He used half of his gas driving back and forth to school, 5 gallons driving to work, and 2 gallons running errands. He had 1 gallon left by the end of the week. How much gas does his tank hold? 5 + 2 + 1 = 8; He used half of the gas going to school, so 2 × 8 = 16 gallons

Intervention Lesson **J29**

Name ____________________

Intervention Lesson J29

Make a Graph

Materials crayons or markers, grid paper

Students in two classes voted on the type of booth they would like to sponsor at the carnival. The results are in the tally charts below. Answer 1 to 4 to find which type of booth the two classes should sponsor together.

Mrs. Bentley's Class

Carnival Booth	Tally
Balloon Pop	𝍸 IIII
Ring Toss	𝍸 III
Face Painting	IIII

Mr. Chavez's Class

Carnival Booth	Tally
Balloon Pop	𝍸
Ring Toss	𝍸 III
Face Painting	𝍸 III

1. Draw a bar graph of each set of data.

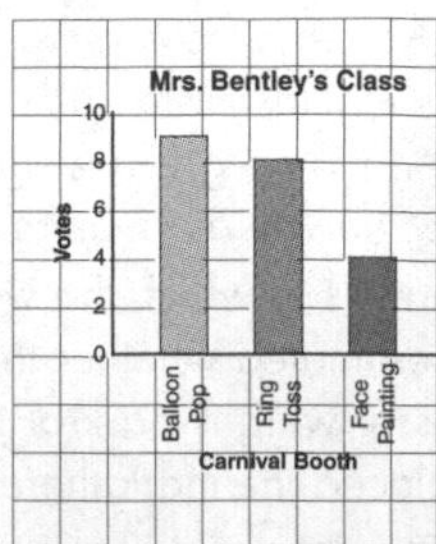

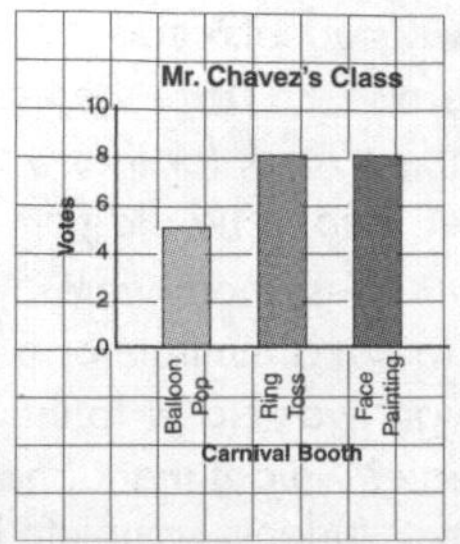

 J29 (student p. 1) MDIS 2.0

Name ____________________

Intervention Lesson J29

Make a Graph (continued)

2. What was the least favorite type of booth of the students in Mrs. Bentley's Class? face painting
3. What was the least favorite type of booth of the students in Mr. Chavez's Class? balloon pop
4. **Reasoning** Which type of booth should the two classes sponsor together? Explain your choice.
   Sample answer: Ring toss; Ring toss was not the least favorite of either class and a lot of students in both classes chose it.

Two classes voted on which type of seed they would like to plant in their garden. The results are shown in the tally charts below. Use the information in the tally charts for 5-8.

Ms. Aydin's Class

Type of Seed	Tally
Pumpkin	𝍸 𝍸
Cantaloupe	𝍸 II
Watermelon	𝍸

Mr. Brown's Class

Type of Seed	Tally
Pumpkin	𝍸 𝍸
Cantaloupe	IIII
Watermelon	𝍸 III

5. Draw a horizontal bar graph of the results for each class. Use grid paper.
   Graphs are shown on the Teacher Notes page.
6. Which seed got the same number of votes from both classes? pumpkin
7. Cantaloupe got more votes from which class? Ms. Aydin's Class
8. **Reasoning** Was the favorite seed the same for both classes? Explain how you can tell from the graphs.
   Yes, pumpkin was the favorite of both classes. The bar for pumpkin was the longest on both graphs.

 J29 (student p. 2) MDIS 2.0

Objective Students will make a graph to represent data.
Vocabulary Bar graph, horizontal bar graph
Materials Crayons or markers, grid paper

1 Conceptual Development

Use with Exercises 1–4.

In this lesson you will learn to make a graph to represent data.

Revisit the terms *bar graph* and *horizontal bar graph* as needed. Have students read the problem and complete Exercise 1. *What does each square on the grid represent in your graph?* Each square represents one vote. Have students complete Exercises 2–4. *How do the two graphs compare with each other: what is similar and what is different?* Both classes have a high vote for Ring Toss, but one class has a higher vote for Balloon Pop while the other class has an equal vote for Face Painting.

2 Practice Use with Exercises 5–8.

Remind students to plan what their key will be if each tally is not represented by one square.

Error Intervention If students have difficulty making graphs to represent data, provide them with strips of paper to represent the tally marks and linking cubes to make a physical graph. As they remove each strip of paper, have them add a cube.

If You Have More Time Have students create their own survey, collect the data, and ask a partner to make a graph showing their data.

3 Assessment

In this lesson students learned to make a graph to represent collected data. Use the **Quick Check** problem to assess students' understanding.

Quick Check 

Look at the graphs in Exercise 1. How many more students chose the Balloon Pop in Mrs. Bentley's class than chose the Face Painting in Mr. Chavez's class?
1 student

Name ______________________________

Make a Graph

Intervention Lesson **J30**

Will's family has two dogs. The tables below show how each of the two dogs grew as puppies in their first 5 months. How does the growth of the two puppies compare?

Socks' Growth	
Month	**Weight (pounds)**
1	2
2	5
3	10
4	8
5	15

Buddy's Growth	
Month	**Weight (pounds)**
1	2
2	6
3	9
4	15
5	20

You can solve by making and interpreting two line graphs. Answer 1 to 6.

1. Make a line graph of each set of data.

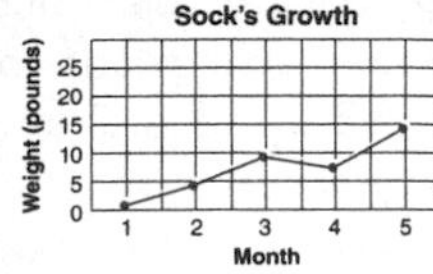

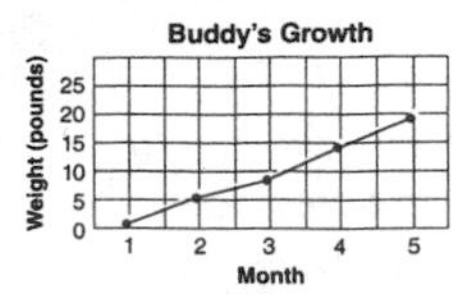

2. Which puppy had the most steady weight gain? Buddy
3. Which puppy had the greatest weight gain in one month? Socks
4. Which puppy lost weight one month? Socks
5. **Reasoning** Which full grown dog probably weighs the most? Why?
   Buddy; Sample answer: Buddy had the greatest overall weight gain in the first 5 months.

Name ______________________________

Make a Graph (continued)

Intervention Lesson **J30**

Answer 6 to **look back at and extend** the problem.

6. **Reasoning** How did the line graphs help you compare the growth of the two puppies?
   Sample answer: The line graphs show the trends in the data. With the graphs side-by-side, it is easier to compare the trends.
7. The data in the two tables below show the gallons of apple and orange juice sold by a company each day for a week. Make a bar graph of each set of data.

Apple Juice Sales	
Day	**Gallons**
Sunday	4
Monday	8
Tuesday	10
Wednesday	14
Thursday	18
Friday	7
Saturday	9

Orange Juice Sales	
Day	**Gallons**
Sunday	6
Monday	8
Tuesday	10
Wednesday	12
Thursday	14
Friday	16
Saturday	18

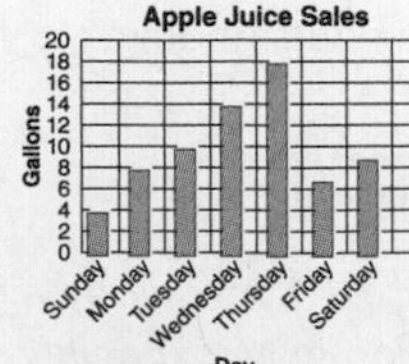

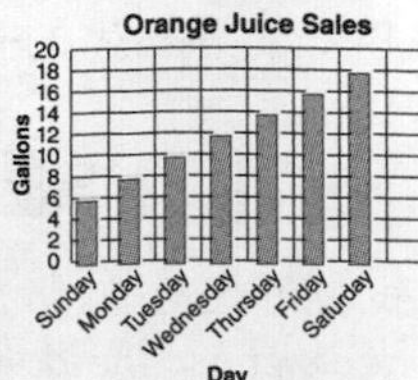

Use the bar graphs above for Exercises 8 to 10.

8. Which type of juice had a steady increase in sales? orange juice
9. Between which two days did the sales of apple juice decrease? between Thursday and Friday
10. On which two days did the company sell a lot more orange juice than apple juice? Friday and Saturday

Objective Students will make and interpret graphs.
Vocabulary Bar graph, line graph

1 Conceptual Development

Use with Exercises 1–6.

In this lesson you will learn to make and interpret graphs.

Revisit the terms *line graph* and *bar graph* as needed. Have students read the problem and complete Exercise 1. *Were there any months that you had to make a mark for that were not on a given weight line? If so, how did you decide where to make the mark?* Yes, there were 5 months in which the weights were not a multiple of 5. I estimated whether the weight was closer to the lesser weight mark or the greater weight mark and placed the mark there. Have students complete Exercises 2–5. *What would it mean if there were a drop in one of the lines between months?* It would mean the puppy lost weight. Have students discuss responses to Exercise 6.

2 Practice **Use with Exercises 7–10.**

Remind students that because each square on the graph in Exercise 7 represents 2, not 1, they will sometimes have to draw a bar past the line.

Error Intervention If students have difficulty transferring data from the chart to the graph, provide them with colored linking cubes and correlating crayons. As they build each bar with cubes, use the same color crayon to shade the data in the graph.

If You Have More Time Have students create their own survey, collect the data, develop five questions, and ask a partner to create either a bar graph, line graph, or vertical bar graph to solve.

3 Assessment

In this lesson students learned to make and interpret graphs. Use the **Quick Check** problem to assess students' understanding.

Look at the graphs you made in Exercise 7. How many more gallons of apple juice were sold on Thursday than gallons of orange juice? 4 gallons

ANALYZE RELATIONSHIPS

Intervention Lesson **J31**

Name ____________________

Intervention Lesson **J31**

Analyze Relationships

Materials cubes, 20 for each student or pair

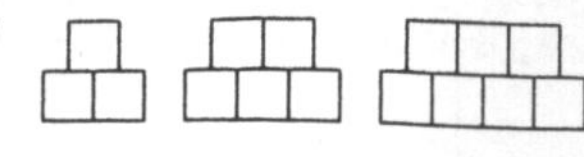

Bob is building a brick wall. He is using a growing pattern as shown to the right. If the pattern continues, how many bricks will be in the sixth design?

Solve by answering 1 to 6.

Answer 1 and 2 to **understand** the problem.

1. What do you know from looking at the diagram?

   The first three designs have <u>3</u>, <u>5</u>, and <u>7</u> bricks.

2. What do you need to find?
   The number of bricks in the sixth design

Answer 3 to 5 to **plan and solve** the problem.

You can solve the problem by finding a pattern.

3. Use cubes to create each design, in order. How many more cubes do you need to use for each new design?
   2 cubes

4. Continue the pattern. Use cubes if you like.

   3, 5, 7, <u>9</u>, <u>11</u>, <u>13</u>

5. How many bricks are in the sixth design?
   13 bricks

Answer 6 through 8 to **look back** at how you solved the problem.

6. **Reasoning** What was the pattern?
   Each time, 2 more bricks were added to the design.

7. How many bricks will be in the tenth design?
   21 bricks

8. If each cube represents 1 cubic unit, what is the volume of the sixth design?
   13 cubic units

Name ____________________

Intervention Lesson **J31**

Analyze Relationships (continued)

Amanda is building a pattern with cubes. If the pattern continues, how many cubes will be in her fourth design?

Solve by answering 9 through 13. Use the diagram to the right.

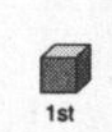
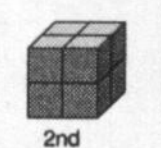

9. How many layers are in the third design?
   3 layers

10. How many cubes are in each layer of the third design?
    9 cubes

11. How many layers will be in the fourth design?
    4 layers

12. How many cubes will be in each layer of the fourth design?
    16 cubes

13. How many cubes will be in the fourth design?
    64 cubes

Answer 14 as an extension to Exercises 9 through 13. Use the diagram above to help.

14. If each cube has a volume of 1 cubic centimeter, what is the volume of each of the 3 designs shown in the pattern?
    1 cm^3; 8 cm^3; 27 cm^3

Use cubes to answer 15.

15. **Reasoning** One rectangular prism has 4 cubes in each of 3 layers. Another rectangular prism has 3 cubes in each of 4 layers. Which rectangular prism has the greater volume?
    The volumes are equal.

Objective Students will use given information to analyze relationships and solve problems.
Vocabulary Cubic centimeter, cubic unit, layer, rectangular prism, volume
Materials Cubes, 20 for each student or pair

1 Conceptual Development

Use with Exercises 1–8.

In this lesson you will learn to use information to analyze relationships and solve problems.

Have students read the problem and look at the diagram at the top of the page. Revisit the terms *cubic centimeter, cubic unit, layer, rectangular prism,* and *volume* as needed. Have students complete Exercises 1 and 2. *How many bricks are in the first diagram?* 3 *The second diagram?* 5 *How about the third diagram?* 7 *What does the question at the top of the page ask us to find?* The number of bricks in the sixth design How many more bricks did you use for each design? 2 Have students complete Exercises 3–8.

2 Practice

Use with Exercises 9–15.

Help students interpret each design as a stacking of layers. Explain that the information students need to solve the problems can be found in the diagrams.

Error Intervention If students have difficulty analyzing relationships, provide additional cubes so they can first create the patterns in the diagrams, count the numbers of cubes they use, and then make each new design discussed in the examples.

If You Have More Time Have students solve the following problem: *Marco has made a rectangular prism using 5 cubes in each of 3 layers. What is the volume of the prism?* 15 cubic units *If each cube represents a volume of 1 cubic meter, what is the volume of the prism?* 15 cubic meters

3 Assessment

In this lesson students learned to analyze relationships and solve problems. Use the **Quick Check** problem to assess students' understanding.

Quick Check  **Formative** Assessment

If you know that the first three designs in a pattern have 4, 7, and 10 cubes, how many cubes would the fourth and fifth designs have? 13; 16

MAKE AND TEST GENERALIZATIONS

Intervention Lesson **J32**

Name ____________

Make and Test Generalizations

Intervention Lesson J32

How are the polygons alike?

Polygon 1 Polygon 2 Polygon 3

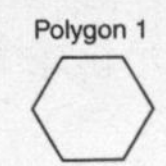  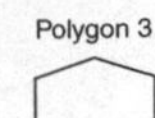

Solve by answering 1 to 5.

1. Complete the generalization about the polygons.

   All the polygons have __6__ sides.

2. Test the generalization.

   Does Polygon 1 have 6 sides? __yes__ Polygon 2? __yes__

   Polygon 3? __yes__

   Since the generalization holds for all 3 polygons, it is true.

3. Test the following generalization: All the sides of each polygon are the same length.

   Are all the sides of Polygon 1 the same length? __yes__

   Are all the sides of Polygon 2 the same length? __no__

   Are all the sides of Polygon 3 the same length? __yes__

4. Is the conjecture true? __no__

5. **Reasoning** Is the following generalization true? All the polygons have at least one obtuse angle. Explain.
   Yes; Sample answer: Polygon 1 has obtuse angles, Polygon 2 has obtuse angles, and Polygon 3 has obtuse angles. The conjecture holds for all 3 polygons, so it is true.

 J32 (student p. 1) MDIS 2.0

Name ____________

Make and Test Generalizations (continued)

Intervention Lesson J32

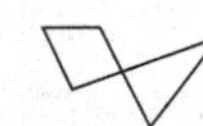 

Make a generalization about each set of figures. Test your generalization. If the generalization is not true, make another generalization until you find one that is true.

6. Sample answer: They all have intersecting lines.

7. N F A Z Y
   Sample answer: They are all made from 3 line segments.

8. Sample answer: They all have 1 right angle.

9. Sample answer: They are all rectangles.

10. Sample answer: They all include a curved side.

 J32 (student p. 2) MDIS 2.0

Objective Students will make and test generalizations.
Vocabulary Polygon

1 Conceptual Development
Use with Exercises 1–5.

In this lesson you will learn to make and test generalizations.

Revisit the term *polygon* as needed. Have students look at the polygons and complete Exercises 1–2. *Are the number of sides the same for each polygon?* Yes Have students complete Exercises 3–5. *Which polygon has sides of different lengths?* Polygon 2 *How could you test the generalization in Exercise 5 to prove it to be right or wrong?* I could measure all of the angles in each polygon.

2 Practice **Use with Exercises 6–10.**

Remind students that for a generalization to be true, it must apply to every item in the group.

Error Intervention If students have difficulty understanding whether generalizations are true, provide them with a concrete set of items and have them make up correct and incorrect generalizations about them.

If You Have More Time Have students work in pairs or groups to find four objects in the room, create two true and two false generalizations about the set, and share with the class.

3 Assessment

In this lesson students learned to make and test generalizations. Use the **Quick Check** problem to assess students' understanding.

Quick Check  **Formative** Assessment

Draw the shapes below on the board. *Danielle says that all of these shapes have at least one 90° angle. Explain whether she is correct.*

Danielle is not correct because the third shape does not have any 90° angles.

MAKE AND TEST CONJECTURES

Name ______________________

Make and Test Conjectures

Intervention Lesson J33

If a number n is a factor of a number m, what is true about the factors of n and m?

Solve by answering 1 to 5.

Start by looking at some examples and making a conjecture.

1. The table below has some examples for m and n. Notice each value of n is a factor of the value of m in the same row. Complete the table.

m	Factors of m	n	Factors of n
12	1, 2, 3, 4, 6, 12	6	1, 2, 3, 6
28	1, 2, 4, 7, 14, 28	14	1, 2, 7, 14
24	1, 2, 3, 4, 6, 8, 12, 24	12	1, 2, 3, 4, 6, 12
36	1, 2, 3, 4, 6, 9, 12, 18, 36	12	1, 2, 3, 4, 6, 12
36	1, 2, 3, 4, 6, 9, 12, 18, 36	18	1, 2, 3, 6, 9, 18

2. Complete the conjecture.

   If a number n is a factor of a number m, then all the factors of __n__ are factors __m__.

A **counterexample**, is an example which proves a conjecture is not true.

3. Try to find a counterexample for your conjecture. List the numbers you try.
   Answers will vary, but make sure one number is a factor of the other in each pair.

   _____ and _____ _____ and _____ _____ and _____

4. Could you find a counterexample? __no__

A counterexample can prove a conjecture is false, but it cannot prove that a conjecture is true.

5. Is your conjecture proven false? __no__ Is it proven true? __no__

Name ______________________

Make and Test Conjectures (continued)

Intervention Lesson J33

Make and test a conjecture about the factors of n and twice n by answering 6 to 9.

6. Complete the table. Look for a pattern.

n	Number of Factors of n	$2n$	Number of Factors of $2n$
6	4	12	6
14	4	28	6
12	6	24	8
40	8	80	10

7. Complete the conjecture.

   The number that is twice n has __2__ more factors than n.

8. Try to find a counterexample for your conjecture. Either give the counterexample or list at least 3 sets of numbers you try.
   Answers may vary. One counterexample is 18 and 36. 18 has 6 factors. Twice 18, or 36, has 9 factors, which is not 2 more than 6.

9. Is your conjecture proven false? __yes__ Is it proven true? __no__

Write a conjecture to answer each question.

10. How are the patterns alike?

    Benita's pattern is: 2, 4, 6, 8, 10, 12, 14, ...

    Carol's pattern is: 1, 3, 5, 7, 9, 11, 13, ...

    Sample answer: They both add 2.

11. How did Beth sort the shapes into Groups A and B?
    Sample answer: All the shapes in Group A have 4 sides and all the shapes in Group B have 5 sides.

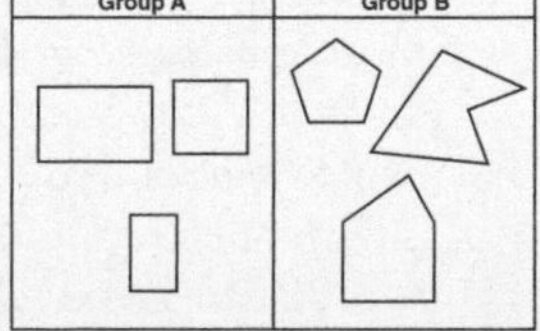

12. Make another conjecture about how Beth sort the shapes.
    Sample answer: All the shapes in Group A have two sets of parallel sides and none of the shapes in Group B have two sets of parallel sides.

Objective Students will make and test conjectures.
Vocabulary Conjecture, counterexample

1 Conceptual Development
Use with Exercises 1–5.

In this lesson you will learn to make and test conjectures.

Discuss the terms *conjecture* and *counterexample* as needed, and have students define the terms in their own words. Read the first problem with students. Have students complete Exercises 1–2. *What do you notice about the two sets of factors?* All of the factors of n are factors of m in the same row. Have students complete Exercises 3–5. *Why do you think that a counterexample cannot prove a conjecture to be true?* Since you cannot test every possibility of a conjecture, there is always a chance that there will be an instance where it is false.

2 Practice **Use with Exercises 6–12.**

Remind students that a counterexample cannot be used to prove that something is true; it can only be used to prove that something is false.

Error Intervention If students have difficulty understanding whether conjectures are true, provide them with real-world examples that they can physically prove to be true or false.

If You Have More Time Have students work in pairs or groups to create a situation that is either true or false and to provide reasons to back their statements.

3 Assessment

In this lesson students learned to make and test conjectures. Use the **Quick Check** problem to assess students' understanding.

Quick Check 

Ethan made a conjecture that if you divide a number by a greater number that is x times itself, you get a fraction, except for zero. Give two examples explaining whether Ethan is correct. He is correct; $12 \div 24 = \frac{1}{2}$, $14 \div 42 = \frac{1}{3}$.

Name ______________________

Reasonableness

Intervention Lesson **J34**

A container when empty weighs 150 pounds. If the container is filled with 312 pounds, what is the total weight of the container and its contents?

Solve by answering 1 to 7.

Answer 1 and 2 to **understand** the problem.

1. What do you know from reading the problem?

   The empty container weighs __150__ pounds.

   The contents of the container weighs __312__ pounds.

2. What do you need to find?

   What is the total weight of the container and its contents?

Answer 3 and 4 to **plan and solve** the problem.

3. How can you solve the problem? __Add 150 and 312.__

4. What is the total weight of the container and its contents? __462__ pounds

Answer 5 to 7 to **check** that your answer is reasonable.

5. Estimate 150 + 312 by rounding to the nearest hundred.

   150 + 312 is about __500__

6. Is your answer to the problem close to the estimate? __yes__

Since the answer of 462 is close to the estimate of 500, the answer 462 pounds is **reasonable**.

7. Did you answer the right question? __yes__

 J34 (student p. 1) MDIS 2.0

Name ______________________

Reasonableness (continued)

Intervention Lesson **J34**

Solve each problem. Then explain why your answer is reasonable.

8. Karen had some stickers. She gave 34 butterfly stickers and 27 flag stickers to Bill. How many stickers did Karen give to Bill?

   Karen gave Bill 51 stickers. 34 + 27 is about 30 + 20 = 50. Since 51 is close to 50, the answer of 51 is reasonable.

9. Harold collects stamps. He has 32 stamps from the United States and 18 stamps from other countries. How many more United States stamps does Harold have than international stamps?

   Harold has 14 more United States stamps than international stamps. 32 − 18 is about 30 − 20 = 10. Since 14 is close to 10, the answer of 14 is reasonable.

10. Some students took a survey about cats and dogs. They found that 87 students like dogs and 56 students like cats. How many students voted for cats or dogs?

    143 students; 87 + 56 is about 90 + 60 = 150. Since 143 is close to 150, the answer of 143 is reasonable.

11. On Friday, 214 people came to the concert. On Saturday, 298 people came. How many people came on both nights combined?

    512 people; 214 + 298 is about 200 + 300 = 500. Since 512 is close to 500, the answer of 512 is reasonable.

12. At TV City, a new television costs $629. At Discount Place, the same TV costs $498. How much more does the TV cost at TV City than at Discount Place?

    $131; 629 − 498 is about 600 − 500 = 100. Since 131 is close to 100, the answer of 131 is reasonable.

 J34 (student p. 2) MDIS 2.0

Objective Students will use estimation to check for reasonableness of answers.

Vocabulary Reasonable

1 Conceptual Development

Use with Exercises 1–7.

In this lesson you will learn to use estimation to check for reasonableness of answers.

Discuss the term *reasonable.* Have students read the problem and complete Exercises 1–2. *How will you use the information you know from the problem?* I will use the weights to find the total weight of the container and its contents. Have students complete Exercises 3–7. *How does estimating help you to see whether your answer is reasonable?* If my answer is near my estimation, then I know it should be correct.

2 Practice

Use with Exercises 8–12.

Remind students that estimating will help them to see whether their answer is reasonable.

Error Intervention If students have difficulty understanding how to determine reasonableness, provide them with real-world situations where estimating will help them know whether their answers are close to correct.

If You Have More Time Have students develop situations where estimations are acceptable and situations where exact answers are needed.

3 Assessment

In this lesson students learned to use estimation to check for reasonableness of answers. Use the **Quick Check** problem to assess students' understanding.

Quick Check

Solve and explain whether your answer is reasonable: Elton is having an end-of-year party for gymnastics. He has 38 gymnasts who are all bringing their family. Most families have 4 people in them. He is planning on about 250 guests at the party. Is Elton's estimation of the number of guests reasonable? No, his estimate is high. If there are 4 people per 38 gymnasts, 4 × 38 = 152 people. If he rounds to estimate, 4 × 40 = 160 people, which is not close to 250.

Name ______

Reasonableness

Intervention Lesson J35

Ahmed has 183 postcards in his collection. He mounts them on sheets of poster board, with 12 postcards on each board. How many sheets of poster board does he need to mount all of his postcards?

Solve by answering 1 to 7.

Answer 1 and 2 to **understand** the problem.

1. What do you know from reading the problem?

   Ahmed has 183 postcards.

   Ahmed puts 12 postcards on each sheet of poster board.

2. What do you need to find?
   How many sheets of poster board does Ahmed need to mount all of his postcards?

Answer 3 and 4 to **plan and solve** the problem.

You can solve by drawing a picture.

3. How can you solve the problem? Divide 183 by 12.
4. How many sheets of poster board does Ahmed need to mount all of his postcards? 16.

Answer 5 to 7 to **check** that your answer is reasonable.

5. Did you answer the right question? Explain.
   Yes; Sample answer: $183 \div 12 = 15$ R3. However, 15 sheets of poster board are not enough, so Ahmed needs 16 to mount all of his postcards, which is the question asked.

6. Estimate $183 \div 12$. $183 \div 12$ is between 10 and 20.

Name ______

Reasonableness (continued)

Intervention Lesson J35

7. Is your answer between the numbers in the estimate? yes

Since the answer of 16 is between 10 and 20, the answer 16 is **reasonable**.

Solve each problem. Then explain why your answer is reasonable.

8. A swimming pool is 11 meters wide and 38 meters long. What is the area of the swimming pool?
   418 square meters; 11×38 is about $10 \times 40 = 400$. Since 418 is close to 400, the answer of 418 is reasonable.
9. The 272 students at Crestwood School are going on a field trip to the art museum. If the students travel in 6 buses, how many students are on each bus?
   2 buses have 46 students and 4 buses have 45 students; $270 \div 6$ is between $240 \div 6 = 40$ and $300 \div 6 = 50$. Since 45 and 46 are between 40 and 50, the answers of 45 and 46 are reasonable.
10. For lunch, Jason bought a chicken sandwich for \$3.25, a carton of milk for \$1.10, and a cookie for \$0.50. How much did he spend?
    \$4.85; \$3.25 + \$1.10 + \$0.50 is about \$3 + \$1 + \$1 = \$5. Since \$4.85 is close to \$5, the answer of \$4.85 is reasonable.
11. Tina has a board 16 feet long. She is going to cut as many 3-foot shelves from the board as she can. How much of the board will she have left?
    1 foot; Sample answer: $16 \div 3 = 5$R1. Since the question asks how much board Tina will have left, the answer is the remainder. I answered the right question.
12. Mr. Rohrs knows that it takes 7 bricks to cover 1 square foot of surface area. How many bricks will he need to construct the wall shown?

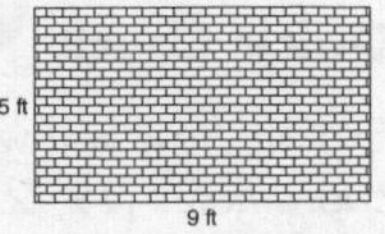

    315 bricks; The area is 45 square feet. 7×45 is about $7 \times 50 = 350$. Since 315 is close to 350, the answer of 315 is reasonable.

Objective Students will use estimation to check for reasonableness of answers.
Vocabulary Reasonable

1 Conceptual Development
Use with Exercises 1–7.

In this lesson you will learn to use estimation to check for reasonableness of answers.

Revisit the term *reasonable*. Have students read the problem and complete Exercises 1–2. *How will you use the information you know from the problem?* I will use the total number of postcards and the number of postcards on each poster board to find how many poster boards Ahmed needs. Have students complete Exercises 3–7. *Which did you find to be an easier way to solve this problem: using division or drawing a picture?* Answers will vary. *How does estimating help you to see whether your answer is reasonable?* If my answer is near my estimation, then I know my answer should be correct.

2 Practice Use with Exercises 8–12.

Remind students that estimating before solving a problem can also help them to see whether their answer is going to be correct as they are solving the problem.

Error Intervention If students have difficulty understanding how to determine reasonableness, explain how an estimate can help them evaluate whether their answer is correct.

If You Have More Time Have pairs create four situations or problems that need to be solved and then checked for reasonableness.

3 Assessment

In this lesson students learned to use estimation to check for reasonableness of answers. Use the **Quick Check** problem to assess students' understanding.

Quick Check  **Formative** Assessment

Solve and explain whether your answer is reasonable: Heidi is making a flower bed for her mother. It is 12 feet wide and 24 feet long. What is the perimeter of the flower bed? $12 + 12 + 24 + 24 = 72$ feet; Explanations of resonableness will vary.

Name ______________________

Intervention Lesson **J36**

Use Representations

Eric walked to Kim's house to return a book that he had borrowed. Eric stayed at Kim's house for a few minutes and then walked home.

The graph at the right represents the distance Eric walked and how long it took Eric to walk to Kim's house and then back home.

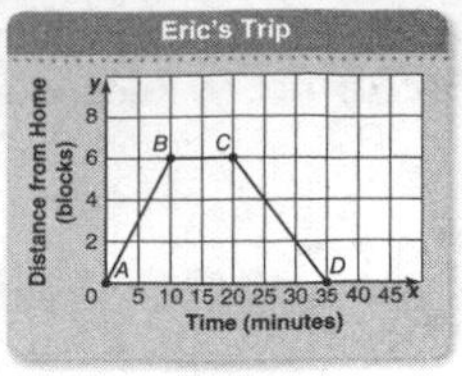

Eric's Trip

Use the graph to answer 1 to 7.

1. Eric left home at Point *A* and arrived at Kim's house at Point *B*. How long did it take Eric to walk to Kim's house?
   10 minutes
2. How far is Kim's house from Eric's house?
   6 blocks
3. Which part of the graph represents the time that Eric was at Kim's house?
   The part between Points *B* and *C*
4. Which part of the graph represents the time it took Eric to walk home?
   The part between Points *C* and *D*
5. Did Eric walk faster to Kim's house or back home to his own house? Explain.
   Eric walked faster to Kim's house. It took Eric 10 minutes to walk to Kim's house and 15 minutes to walk home.
6. The ordered pair (10, 6) locates Point *B* on the graph. What ordered pair locates Point *C* on the graph?
   (20, 6)
7. What do the coordinates (35, 0) represent?
   35 represents that Eric's trip took 35 minutes to complete. 0 represents that he is 0 blocks from home, so he must be at home again.

Name ______________________

Intervention Lesson **J36**

Use Representations (continued)

Sarah is sewing buttons on shirts. She began sewing at 10:30 A.M.

The graph at the right represents the number of buttons Sarah sews and the time it takes her to sew them on the shirts.

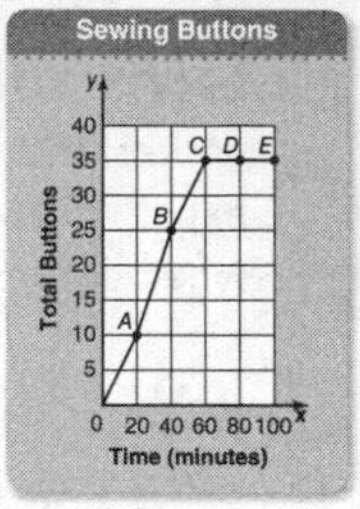

Sewing Buttons

Use the graph to answer 8 to 13.

8. Look at Point *A*. How many buttons did Sarah sew during the first 20 minutes?
   10 buttons
9. What ordered pair locates Point *B* on the graph?
   (40, 25)
10. How many buttons did Sarah sew in all?
    35 buttons
11. Did Sarah sew more buttons in the period of time between Points *A* and *B* or in the period of time between Points *B* and *C*? Explain.
    The time between Points *A* and *B*; Sarah sewed 15 buttons during this period of time compared with 10 buttons for the period of time between Points *B* and *C*.
12. What might have happened between Points *C* and *E*?
    Sample answer: Sarah might have taken a break to eat lunch, so no buttons were sewn during this period of time.
13. Write another story to fit the data on the graph.
    Check students' work. Students' stories should fit the graph.

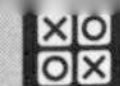

Objective Students will analyze data in graphs.
Vocabulary Ordered pair, coordinates

1 Conceptual Development

Use with Exercises 1–7.

In this lesson you will learn to analyze data in graphs.

Have students look at the graph. Revisit the terms *ordered pair* and *coordinates* as needed. Have students complete Exercise 1. *How did you find the time it took Eric to get to Kim's house?* I found Point *B* on the graph and looked down to find the time in minutes. *What do the numbers in the ordered pair, (10, 6), represent?* The first number represents the *x*-axis (time), and the second represents the *y*-axis (blocks from home). Have students complete Exercises 2–7.

2 Practice Use with Exercises 8–13.

Help students explain what is being displayed on the graph. Remind them that *Time* is the first coordinate and the *Total Buttons* is the second coordinate.

Error Intervention

If students have difficulty with ordered pairs, point out that the letter *O* comes before the letter *U* in the alphabet; so when graphing ordered pairs, first you move Over, and then you go Up.

If You Have More Time

Have students solve the following problem and explain their methods: *If Sarah had stopped sewing after 40 minutes, how many buttons would she have sewn?* 25 *Let us say that Sarah sewed 5 buttons between 60 and 80 minutes. How would the graph change?* Points *D* and *E* would be higher on the graph: at (80, 40) and (100, 40).

3 Assessment

In this lesson students learned to analyze data in graphs. Use the **Quick Check** problem to assess students' understanding.

Quick Check  **Formative** Assessment

Explain how you would locate a point with the coordinates (19, 27) on a graph. Sample answer: The 19 is the *x*-coordinate and the 27 is the *y*-coordinate; I would look along the bottom axis to find the 19, and then I would go up to 27 from there.

Name ______________________

Writing to Explain

Intervention
Lesson J37

Materials crayons or markers

At Sam's Sandwich Shop, Toni ate $\frac{3}{4}$ of a medium sandwich, Becky ate $\frac{3}{4}$ of a small sandwich, and Mary Jo ate $\frac{6}{8}$ of a medium sandwich. Explain why Toni and Mary Jo ate the same amount of sandwich, but Toni and Becky ate different amounts.

Solve by answering 1 to 8.

Toni

Becky

Mary Jo

1. Toni ate $\frac{3}{4}$ of a medium sandwich. Color the diagram at the right to show what Toni ate.
2. Becky ate $\frac{3}{4}$ of a small sandwich.
3. How did the size of Becky's sandwich compare to the size of Toni's sandwich?
   Becky's sandwich was smaller than Toni's
4. Color the diagram above to show what Becky ate.
5. Mary Jo ate $\frac{6}{8}$ of a medium sandwich.
6. How did the size of May Jo's sandwich compare to the size of Toni's sandwich?
   The sandwiches are the same size.
7. Color the diagram above to show what Mary Jo ate.
8. Use the diagram to explain why Toni and Mary Jo ate the same amount, but Toni and Becky ate different amounts.
   Sample answer: The diagram shows that Toni and Mary Jo ate the same amount of sandwich, because $\frac{3}{4}$ and $\frac{6}{8}$ are equivalent fractions and the sandwiches are the same size. The diagram also shows that Toni and Becky ate different amounts because the sandwiches were not the same size.

 J37 (student p. 1) MDIS 2.0

Name ______________________

Writing to Explain (continued)

Intervention
Lesson J37

Write to explain.

9. Explain how you find the perimeter of the figure shown on the right.
   Add the sum of all the sides.
   $8 + 7 + 8 + 9 + 6 + 5 = 43$ ft

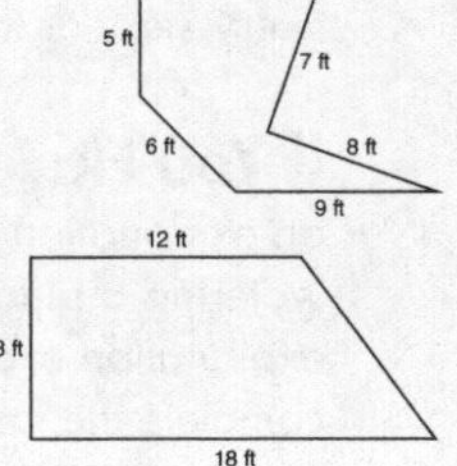

10. Mrs. Kim wants to re-seed a small section of her yard. Explain how to find the area of the yard.
    Divide the figure into a rectangle and a triangle and find the area of each figure.
    $12 \times 8 = 96; \frac{(6 \times 8)}{2} = 24;$
    $96 + 24 = 120$ square feet

Solve the problem. Write to explain how you solved.

11. The Oak Street Theater has 4 sections of seating. Each section has 5 rows of seats. Two sections have 4 seats in each row. The other sections have 3 seats in each row. How many seats are there in the theater?
    70 seats; Sample answer: Two sections have 5 rows with 4 seats in each row, so two sections have 20 seats each. That's 40 seats in all. There are 4 sections in all, so there are 2 more sections. Each of those sections has 5 rows with 3 seats in each row, or 15 seats. That's 30 seats in those two sections. $40 + 30 = 70$ seats in all.

 J37 (student p. 2) MDIS 2.0

Objective Students will use writing to explain their methods when solving a problem.
Materials Crayons or markers

1 Conceptual Development

Use with Exercises 1–8.

In this lesson you will learn to use writing to explain your methods when solving a problem.

Have students complete Exercises 1–8. *What words in the problem give you clues about what you have to prove?* The words *medium sandwich* and *small sandwich* are a clue that the fraction may be the same, but it does not represent parts of the same-sized whole. *How did you work through the problem to explain why the amounts eaten were different?* I colored the diagrams to represent each fraction; I used the sizes of the sandwiches to help me make sense of things; I looked at the diagrams and reread the problem to connect the words with the pictures.

2 Practice Use with Exercises 9–11.

Remind students that thinking about each step as they do it provides them with what they can write when trying to explain their methods.

Error Intervention If students have difficulty writing to explain their methods when solving a problem, have them do a simple task, such as tying their shoes, and write down each step.

If You Have More Time Have one student write out an explanation of how to solve a problem, and have another student follow those instructions completely to see whether he or she gets the same results.

3 Assessment

In this lesson students learned to use writing to explain their methods when solving a problem. Use the **Quick Check** problem to assess students' understanding.

Quick Check  **Formative** Assessment

Solve and write to explain your work: Jen is planning the music banquet. She has 97 people attending. The tables she is using can seat 8 people per table. How many tables will she need to seat all of the guests? $97 \div 8 = 12$ R1, so Jen will need 13 tables. Check validity of students' explanations.

Name ________________________________

Try, Check, and Revise

Materials place-value blocks, 24 unit cubes for each student

Sylvia has 24 small boxes that are each in the shape of a cube. She needs to arrange them to form a larger box in the shape of a rectangular prism. How many different rectangular prisms can Sylvia make with the 24 cubes?

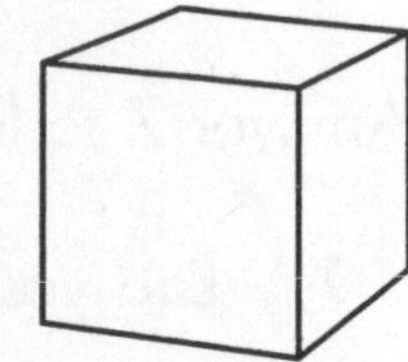

Solve by answering 1 to 7.

Answer 1 and 2 to **understand** the problem.

1. What do you know from reading the problem?

Sylvia has ________ small boxes, each the shape of a ________.

2. What do you need to find?

Answer 3 to 6 to **plan and solve** the problem.

You can solve the problem by using the strategy Try, Check, and Revise.

3. Use the blocks to try a height of 1 and a width of 1. Is it possible to make a rectangular prism? ________

4. What are the prism's dimensions? 1 by 1 by ________

5. Use the blocks to try a height of 1 and a width of 2, then a height of 1 and a width of 3, and so on. Then try a height of 2 and a width of 2, a height of 2 and a width of 3 and so on. List all the dimensions that work. Consider 1 by 2 by 12 the same as 2 by 1 by 12.

Try, Check, and Revise (continued)

6. How many different rectangular prisms can Sylvia make with the 24 cubes? ________

Answer 7 to **look back** at how you solved the problem.

7. Did you answer the right question? ________

Solve each problem.

8. Angus has 22 feet of flower-bed edging. The rectangular shaped flower bed he made is 5 feet longer than it is wide. What are the dimensions of his flower bed?

____

9. Genia has 10 coins that consist of dimes and nickels. She has a total of $0.60. How many does she have of each coin?

____

10. During a visit to the zoo, Mary counted 32 legs. The only animals in the exhibit were ostriches and giraffes. How many of each animal were in the exhibit?

____

11. Nadine wants to build a patio that has an area of 36 square yards. However, she wants the patio to have the smallest perimeter possible. What dimensions should she build her patio?

____

12. Simone bought 20 CDs and paid $149. How many new and how many used CDs did she buy?

CDs
New $12 each
Used $5 each

____

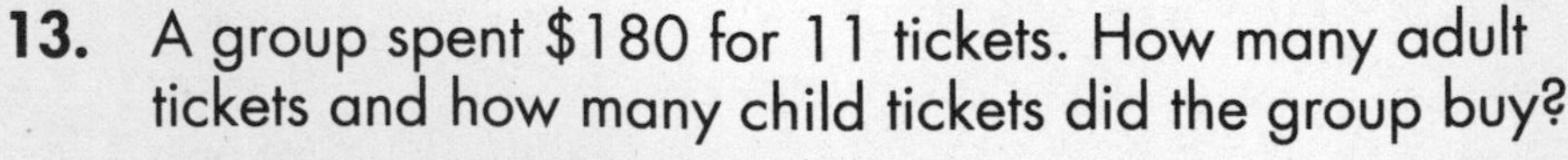

13. A group spent $180 for 11 tickets. How many adult tickets and how many child tickets did the group buy?

TICKETS
adults $18 each
children $12 each

____

Name ________________________________

Solve a Simpler Problem

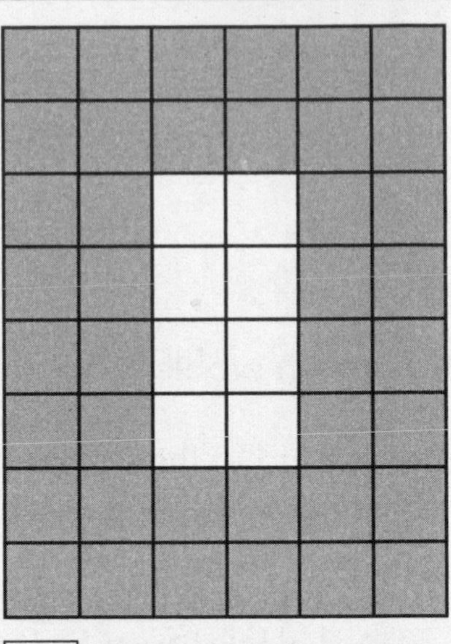

A diagram of a flower garden in the city park is shown on the right. The garden is made of rose bushes and marigolds. The shaded part of the figure shows the part of the garden that is marigolds. What is the area of the shaded part of the flower garden?

Solve by answering 1 to 6.

Answer 1 and 2 to **understand** the problem.

1. What do you know from reading the problem?

The diagram shows a garden. The shaded part shows the part with marigolds.

The rest of the garden has ________.

2. What do you need to find?

Answer 3 to 5 to **plan and solve** the problem.

You can solve the problem by solving two simpler problems first.

3. What is the area of the whole garden?

_____ × _____ = _____

4. What is the area of the part that is not shaded?

_____ × _____ = _____

5. The area of the shaded part is the whole area minus the part that is not shaded. What is the area of the shaded part?

_____ − _____ = _____ square yards

Name ____

Solve a Simpler Problem (continued)

Answer 6 to **look back** at how you solved the problem.

6. Explain how to use Solving a Simpler Problem to solve a problem.

Solve each problem.

Use the grid at the right for Exercises 7 and 8. Be careful, arrows show one-way streets.

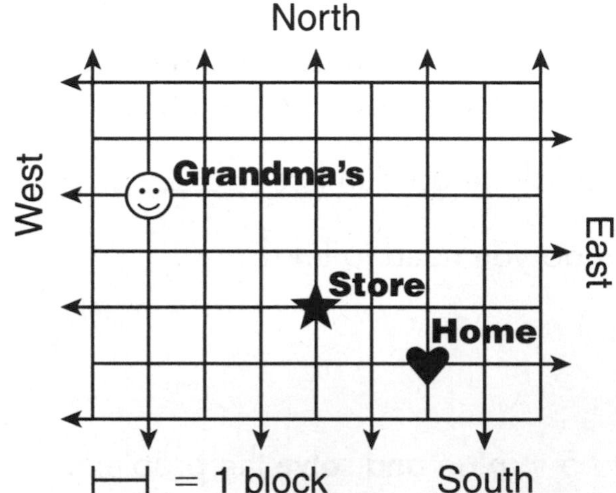

7. Find the distance (the number of blocks) from home to the store and then to Grandma's.

____

8. Sara started from home, drove 5 blocks north, 3 blocks west, and 4 blocks south, but she still needed to go to the store. How many blocks was she from the store?

____

Gloria tiled her bathroom floor. She used white and gray tiles as shown at the right. Use the diagram for Exercises 9 and 10.

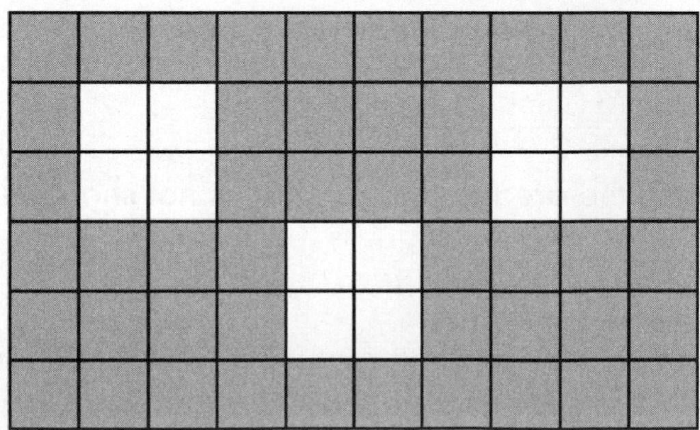

9. What is the gray area?

____

10. How much greater is the gray area than the white area?

____

Name ____________________

Use Representations

The students in Mrs. Nolan's class each collected cans of food to donate. The results are shown in the dot plot at the right.

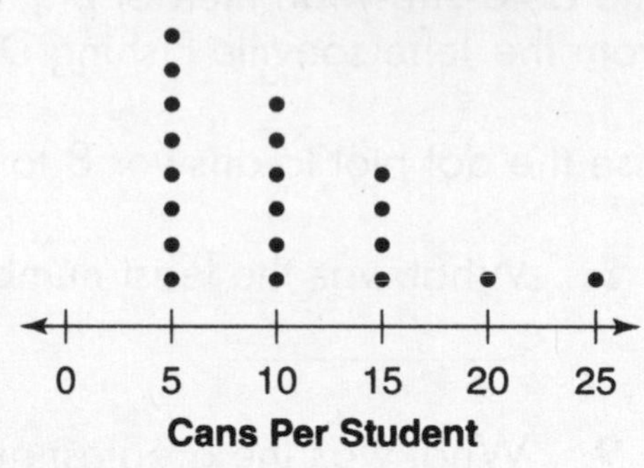

Use the information in the dot plot to answer 1 to 4.

1. How many students collected 15 cans?

   ____

2. How many more students collected 10 cans than 20 cans? ____________

3. How many students collected more than 15 cans?

4. How many cans were collected in all? ____________

Steve kept track of the number of minutes he spent working on homework for the last 10 days. His data is listed in the stem-and-leaf plot at the right.

Time Spent on Homework	
Stem	Leaf
1	0 5 7
2	1 2 4
3	0 6
4	0 3
Key: 1 | 5 = 15 minutes	

Use the stem-and-leaf plot to answer 5 to 7.

5. What is the least amount of time Steve spent working on his homework?

   ____

6. What is the greatest amount of time Steve spent working on his homework?

   ____

7. How many more minutes did Steve spend on his homework for the greatest time spent compared to the least time spent?

   ____

Name ______________________________

Use Representations (continued)

The data shown in the dot plot at the right was collected from the Jeffersonville Fishing Derby.

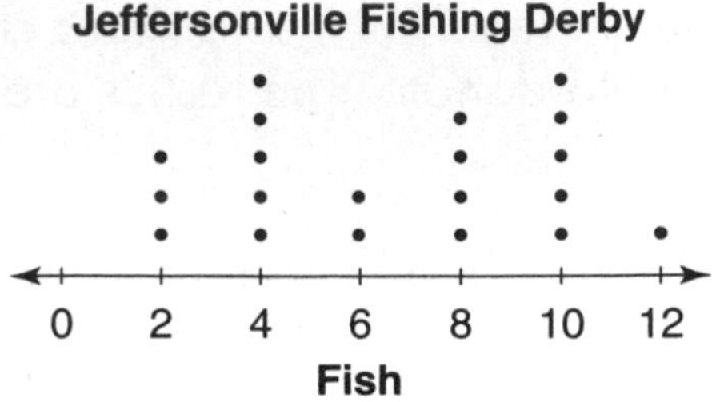

Use the dot plot to answer 8 to 11.

8. What was the least number of fish caught?

____

9. What was the greatest number of fish caught?

____

10. How many more people caught 10 fish than 6 fish?

____

11. Did more people catch less than 6 fish or more than 6 fish? Explain.

Mrs. Wilson collected the scores from her students' latest test. Their scores are shown in the stem-and-leaf plot at the right.

Test Scores	
Stem	Leaf
6	0 3 3 7 7
7	2 2 5 5 8
8	1 4 4 6 9 9 9
9	1 5 8
Key: 7|5 = 75 points	

Use the stem-and-leaf plot to answer 12 to 15.

12. What was the highest test score? __________

13. What was the lowest test score? __________

14. What is the difference between the most points scored and the least points scored on the test? __________

15. How many students took the test? __________

Name ______________________________

Make a Table and Look for a Pattern

Ann and Jane began reading the same book on the same day. If Ann reads 8 pages each day and Jane reads 5 pages each day, what page will Jane read on the day that Ann reads page 40?

Solve by answering 1 to 6.

Answer 1 and 2 to **understand** the problem.

1. What do you know from reading the problem?

Ann reads _______ pages each day.

Jane reads _______ pages each day.

They started the same day.

2. What do you need to find?

Answer 3 to 5 to **plan and solve** the problem.

You can solve the problem by making a table and looking for a pattern.

3. Use patterns to complete the table below.

Day	**1**	**2**	**3**	**4**	**5**	**6**
Ann's Page	8	16				
Jane's Page	5					

4. What day will Ann read page 40? ___________

5. What page will Jane read on the day Ann reads page 40? ___________

Name ______________________________

Make a Table and Look for a Pattern (continued)

Answer 6 to **look back** at your solution.

6. Did you answer the right question? ________

Use patterns to complete each table. Solve each problem.

7. Rebecca must put 4 eggs in each basket. There are 8 baskets. How many eggs does she need? ____________

Number of Baskets	1	2	3	4	5	6	7	8
Number of Eggs	4	8						

8. Martin needs to water each tree with 3 gallons of water. How many gallons of water will he need for 7 trees?

Number of trees	1	2	3	4	5	6	7
Gallons of water							

____

9. Diego recorded the height of a bean plant. The first week, the plant was 2 inches high. The second, third, and fourth week, it was 4 inches, 6 inches, and 8 inches high. At this rate, when will the bean plant be 12 inches high?

Week	1	2	3	4	5	6	7
Height							

____

10. Each quilt square has 2 red sections and 3 blue sections. If 18 blue sections are used, how many red sections are needed?

squares						
red sections						
blue sections						

____

Name ____

Solve a Simpler Problem

Materials color tiles, 10 for each student

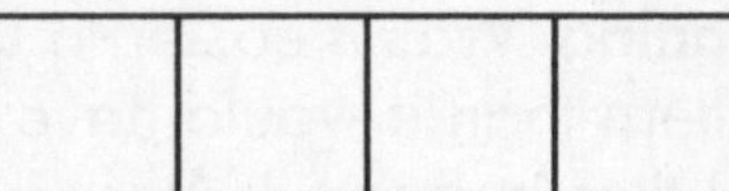

Roger is putting up a row of mirror tiles in his entry way, as show at the right. The tiles are squares, 1 foot on each side. How many feet of wood trim does he need to go around 10 tiles in a row?

Solve by answering 1 to 6.

Answer 1 and 2 to **understand** the problem.

1. What do you know from reading the problem?

The tiles are square and each side is __________ long.

Roger is putting _______ tiles in a row.

2. What do you need to find?

Answer 3 to 5 to **plan and solve** the problem.

You can solve simpler problems, put the solutions in a table, and find a pattern to extend the table in order to solve the problem.

3. Find the feet of trim needed for 3 tiles, 4 tiles, and 5 tiles in a row. You may want to use the picture above. Write the answers in the table below.

Number of tiles	1	2	3	4	5	6	7	8	9	10
Feet of trim	4	6								

4. What is the pattern in the table?

5. Use the pattern to complete the table. How many feet of wood trim does Roger need to go around 10 tiles in a row? __________

Name ______________________________

Solve a Simpler Problem (continued)

Answer 6 to look back at how you solved the problem.

6. **Reasoning** Was it easier to use simpler problems, a table, and a pattern than it would have been to solve by drawing a picture of 10 tiles in a row? What if there were 50 tiles in a row?

Complete each table. Solve each problem.

7. Suppose Mr. Lange had a rope 50 feet long and wanted to cut it into 25 equal pieces. How many cuts would it take?

Pieces	2	3	4	5	6
Cuts	1	2			

____

8. The Washington Stars signed up for a single elimination soccer tournament. This means that 2 teams play and the loser is eliminated. There are 8 entries in the tournament. How many games must be played to determine the champion?

Teams	2	3	4	5	6	7	8
Games	1	2					

____

9. During the grand opening of a craft store, every fourth customer was given a discount coupon. Every tenth customer was given a discount coupon and a gift. During the grand opening, 120 people visited the store. How many coupons and gifts were given away?

Customers	4	8	10	12	16	20	24	28	30	32	36	40
Gifts	0	0	1									
Coupons	1	2	3	4								

____

Name ____________________

Make a Table and Look for a Pattern

Materials 20 unit cubes, for each student

Three fourths of Jamal's CDs are rock and roll. He has 20 or fewer CDs. One way to show $\frac{3}{4}$ is 3 out of 4 equal groups of 5 or $\frac{15}{20}$. Using 20 or fewer cubes, how many other fractions are equivalent to $\frac{3}{4}$?

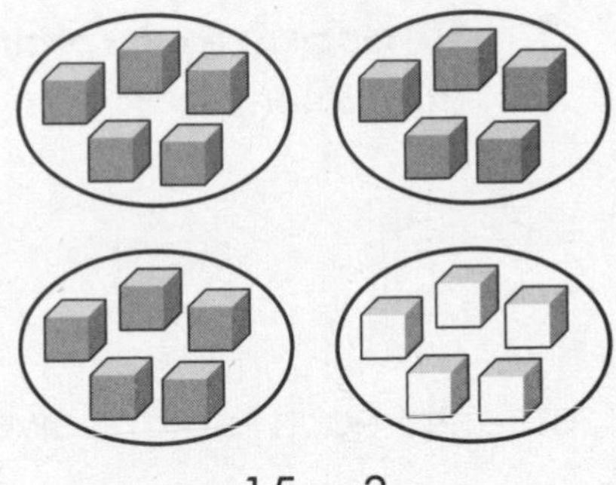

$\frac{15}{20} = \frac{3}{4}$

Solve by answering 1 to 5.

Answer 1 and 2 to **understand** the problem.

1. What do you know from reading the problem?

Jamal has ____________ CDs. ____ of Jamal's CDs are rock and roll.

2. What do you need to find?

Answer 3 and 4 to **plan and solve** the problem.

You can solve the problem by making a table and looking for a pattern.

3. Complete the table. Look for a pattern to help.

4. Using 20 or fewer cubes, how many fractions are equivalent to $\frac{3}{4}$ other than $\frac{15}{20}$?

____

Number of cubes	Cubes in each group	Cubes in 3 groups	Fraction equivalent to $\frac{3}{4}$
20	5	15	$\frac{15}{20}$
			$\frac{9}{12}$

Name ____________________

Make a Table and Look for a Pattern (continued)

Answer 5 to **look back** at how you solved the problem.

5. **Reasoning** Explain how you know you have all the fractions equivalent to $\frac{3}{4}$, using 20 or fewer cubes.

Complete each table. Solve each problem.

6. You are making a bulletin board display of 21 drawings. If you put them in a triangular pattern, how many rows will the drawings make?

Row	1	2	3	4	5	6
Drawings in the Row	1	2	3			
Total Drawings Used	1	3	6			

____

7. Each box lunch has 3 cookies and 4 baby carrots. If 15 cookies are used to make some box lunches, how many baby carrots are used?

Lunch Boxes	1	2	3	4	5	6
Cookies	3	6				
Baby Carrots	4	8				

____

8. Suppose you divide a rectangle with 10 straight lines. What is the greatest number of sections you can form?

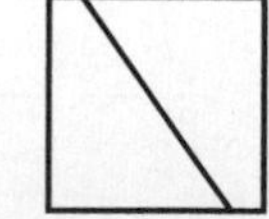
1 line, 2 pieces

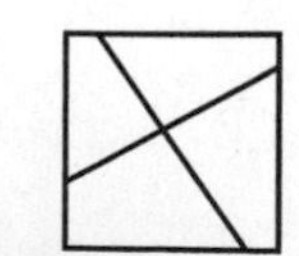
2 lines, 4 pieces

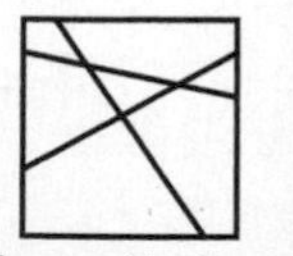
3 lines, 7 pieces

Lines	1	2	3	4	5	6	7	8	9	10
Pieces	1	4								

____

Name ___________________________

Analyze Relationships

Andrea spent $4.25 on wooden sticks and $1.75 on glue to make birdhouses. She sold 3 birdhouses for $2.50 each. How much profit did Andrea make?

Answer 1 and 2 to **understand** the problem.

1. What do you know from reading the problem?

Andrea spent ________ on wooden sticks.

Andrea spent ________ on glue.

Andrea sold ________ birdhouses.

Andrea sold each birdhouse for ________.

2. What do you need to find?

Answer 3 to 5 to **plan and solve** the problem.

3. How can you find the total cost of the materials used to make the birdhouses?

4. How can you find the amount of money Andrea received for selling the 3 birdhouses?

5. How much profit did Andrea make? Use your answers to 3 and 4 to solve.

Name ___________________________________

Analyze Relationships (continued)

Answer 6 to **look back** at how you solved the problem.

6. Explain how you used the total amount of money Andrea spent and received to find how much profit she made.

Solve each problem.

7. Luis spends $7.50 on supplies. He makes and sells 3 items for $5.00 each. What is his profit?

8. Beth spends $3.50 on supplies. She makes and sells 4 items for $2.25 each. What is her profit?

Use the table at the right to answer 9 to 11.

	Jennifer	Michelle
Money Spent	$8.25	$6.85
Money Received	$13.40	$12.35

9. How much is Jennifer's profit?

10. How much is Michelle's profit?

11. **Reasoning** Did Jennifer or Michelle make the greater profit? Explain.

Name ___________________________

Use Objects

Materials color tiles, 16 for each student

Jada bought balloons for the party. She bought red, yellow, and blue balloons. She bought at least one of each color. Use the information at the right to find how many balloons of each color she bought.

Balloons Jada Bought

7 yellow
3 more red than blue
16 balloons in all

Solve by answering 1 to 6.

Answer 1 to 3 to **understand** the problem.

1. What do you know from reading the problem?

Jada bought _______, _______, and _______ balloons.

2. What do you know from reading the chart?

Jada bought _______ yellow balloons.

Jada bought _______ more red balloons than blue balloons.

Jada bought _______ balloons in all.

3. What do you need to find?

Answer 4 and 5 to **plan and solve** the problem.

You can solve the problem by acting out the problem with color tiles.

4. Count out 16 tiles. Separate 7 of them for the yellow balloons. How many red and blue balloons did Jada buy? _______

Name ___________________________________

Use Objects (continued)

5. Separate the tiles representing the red and blue balloons into two piles, so one pile has 3 more tiles than the other. How many balloons of each color did Jada buy?

_______ yellow _______ red _______ blue

Answer 6 to **check** your solution.

6. **Reasoning** Explain why your answer is correct.

Solve each problem.

7. Min is playing with modeling clay. To try to protect the table, his mother put down a plastic placemat. The placemat had 40 small squares on it. How many squares were in each row?

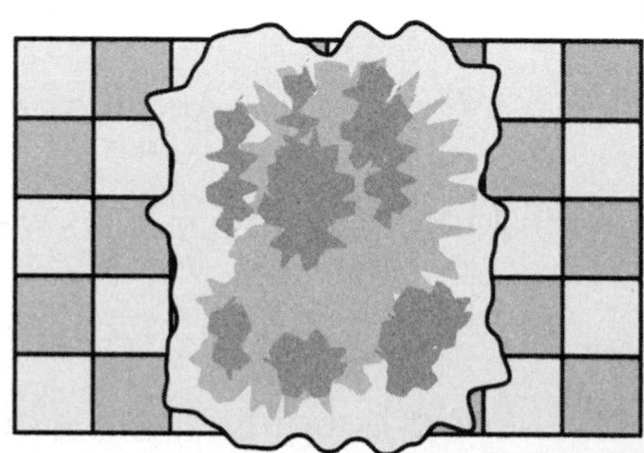

____

8. There are 17 entries in the photo contest. The photos consist of animal photos, nature photos, and portraits. There are 5 portraits. There are 6 fewer nature photos than animal photos. How many of each type of photo was in the contest?

____

9. Tim bought 18 apples for the apple-bobbing contest. He bought red, yellow, and green apples. There are 3 yellow apples. There are twice as many red apples as green apples. How many of each color apple did he buy?

____

Name ______________________________

Use Objects

Intervention Lesson **J22**

Materials color tiles, 6 for each student, crayons, markers, or colored pencils

A hexomino is an arrangement of 6 identical squares that are attached to one another edge to edge. Find 4 different hexominoes, that have 4 squares in a row.

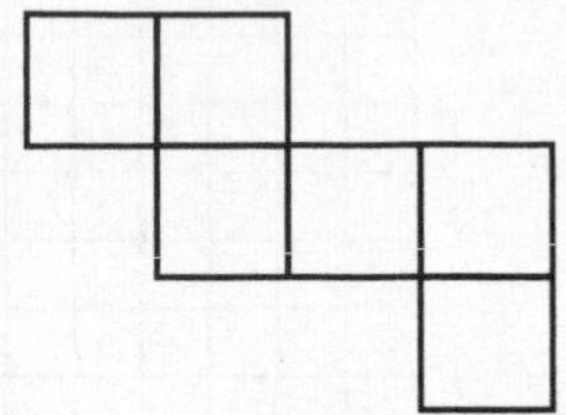
This is a hexomino.

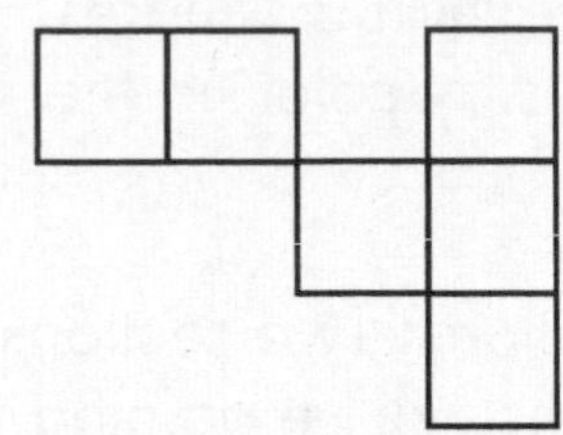
This is not a hexomino.

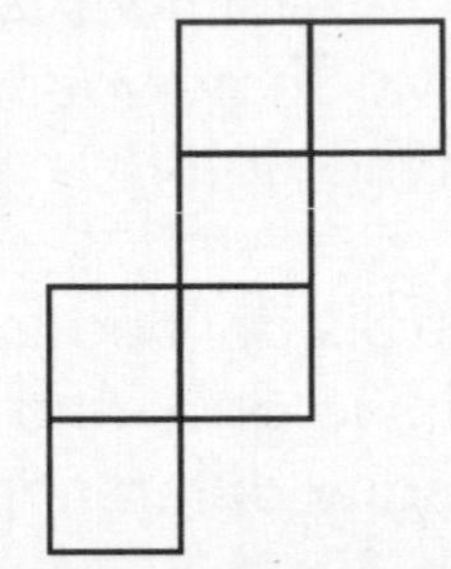
This hexomino is the same as the first one.

Solve by answering 1 to 5.

Answer 1 and 2 to **understand** the problem.

1. What do you know from reading the problem?

A hexomino has _______ identical squares that are attached to one another edge to edge

2. What do you need to find?

Answer 3 and 4 to **plan and solve** the problem.

You can solve the problem by using objects.

3. Put 4 tiles in a row. Add the other two tiles to make a hexomino. Color the grid at the right to show the hexomino you found.

4. Change the tiles to find 3 more hexominos with 4 squares in a row. Color the grid to show each one.

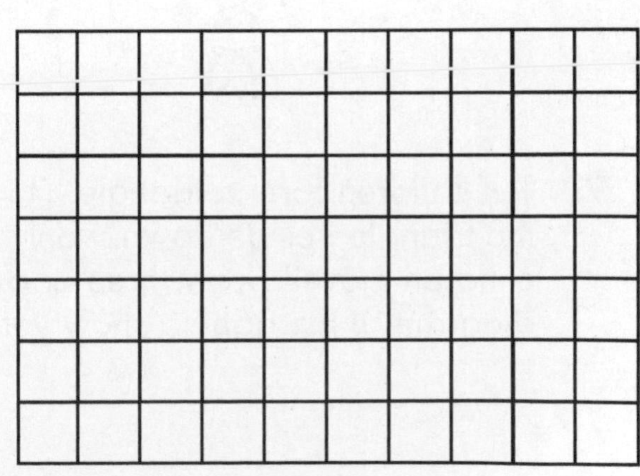

Name ______________________________

Use Objects (continued)

Answer 5 to **look back** at how you solved the problem.

5. Did the color tiles help you solve the problem? ________

Solve each problem.

6. Find 4 hexominoes with no more than 3 squares in a row. Show your hexominoes by coloring the grid at the right.

7. A board is divided into four sections. Two sections will be painted gray and two sections will be painted white. How many different patterns are possible?

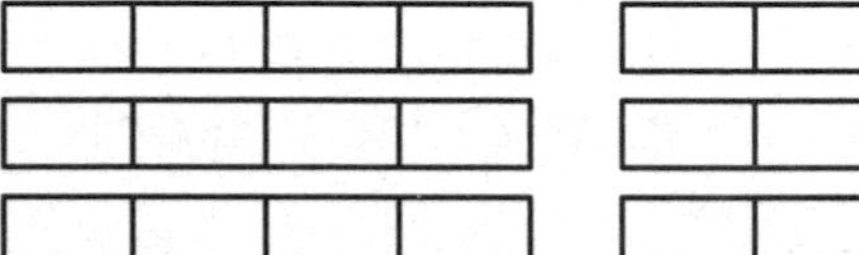

8. Six children form a triangle. How can they turn the triangle upside down if only two of the children move? Draw two arrows on the picture to show your answer.

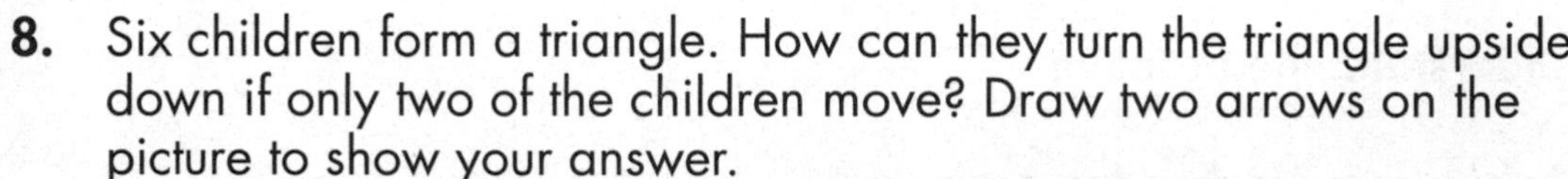

9. Ten children form a triangle. How can they turn the triangle upside down if only three of the children move? Draw three arrows on the diagram at the right to show your answer.

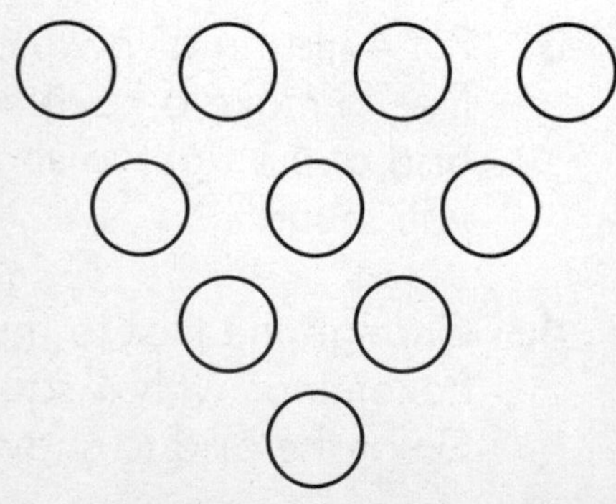

Name ______________________________

Use Reasoning

Materials color tiles, 15 for each student

Laurel has 15 cousins who live in three different states. Three of the cousins live in Montana. Twice as many cousins live in Indiana as live in Wisconsin. How many cousins live in each state?

Solve by answering 1 to 5.

Answer 1 and 2 to **understand** the problem.

1. What do you know from reading the problem?

Laurel has ________ cousins.

Three of Laurel's cousins live in ______________.

________ times as many cousins live in Indiana as live in Wisconsin.

2. What do you need to find?

Answer 3 and 4 to **plan and solve** the problem.

You can solve the problem by using objects and reasoning.

3. Count out 15 tiles. Separate 3 of them for the cousins who live in Montana. How many cousins live in Indiana and Wisconsin combined? ________

4. Separate the tiles representing the cousins who live in Indiana and Wisconsin, so one pile has twice as many tiles as the other. How many of Laurel's cousins live in each state?

________ in Montana ________ in Indiana ________ in Wisconsin

Answer 5 to **look back** at how you solved the problem.

5. **Reasoning** Explain why your answer is correct.

Name ______________________________

Intervention Lesson **J23**

Use Reasoning (continued)

Solve each problem.

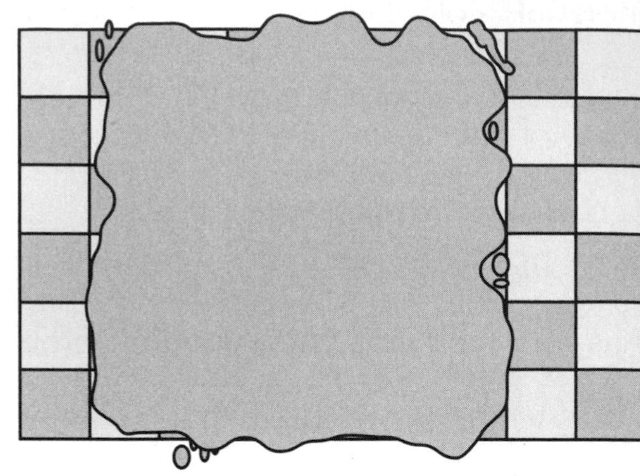

6. Mr. Parvey spilled some cement paint on his patio. Since he was going to paint the patio in a checker board pattern, it was marked in 54 square sections. How many sections were in each row?

____

7. Wanda carries a stack of 17 books. Lyle carries a stack of 11 books. How many books should Wanda give Lyle so they carry the same number? __________

8. Bill, Phillip, and Mandy each have 7 baseball cards. Suppose Bill gives 3 of his to Phillip, and Phillip gives 2 of his to Mandy. How many cards does Phillip have? __________

9. A sporting goods store would like to display a new line of tennis balls in a triangular stack. The bottom row will have 7 canisters and each row going up will have one less canister. How many canisters will be on display? __________

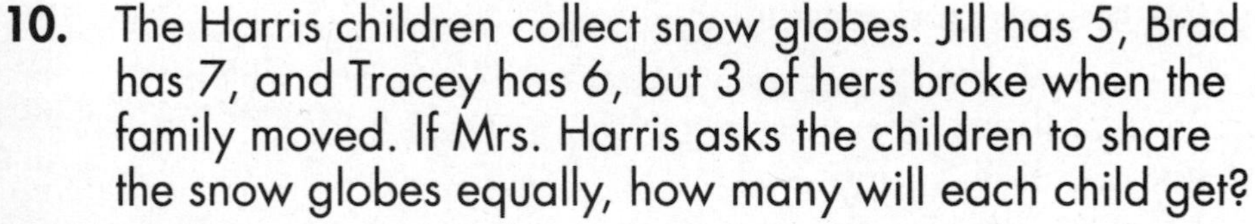

10. The Harris children collect snow globes. Jill has 5, Brad has 7, and Tracey has 6, but 3 of hers broke when the family moved. If Mrs. Harris asks the children to share the snow globes equally, how many will each child get? __________

11. Andrew folds a sheet of paper in half 5 times. When he opens it up, how many sections will there be? __________

12. The perimeter of a rectangular poster is 120 inches. The length of the poster is three times its width. What are the dimensions of the length of the poster?

____

Name ________________________________

Use Reasoning

Intervention Lesson **J24**

Materials place-value blocks, 36 units cubes for each student

Mandy's dad has to stack 36 boxes, in the shape of a rectangular prism, for shipping. All the boxes are the same size cube. He needs to put a sticker on each side of a box that is on the outside when they are stacked, including the bottom. He has 66 stickers. How can he stack the boxes so he has enough stickers?

Solve by answering 1 to 7.

Answer 1 and 2 to **understand** the problem.

1. What do you know from reading the problem?

Mandy's dad has to stack _______ boxes that are all the same size _______.

Mandy's dad has _______ stickers and has to put one on each side of a box that is on the outside when the boxes are stacked.

2. What do you need to find?

Answer 3 to 6 to **plan and solve** the problem.

You can solve by using objects and reasoning.

3. Stack 36 cubes to form a 6 by 2 by 3 rectangular prism. How many sides of a small cube are on the outside of the stack? __________

4. Is the number of sides greater than or less than 66? __________

5. Change the shape of the stack until you get a rectangular prism with 66 or fewer sides on the outside of the stack. What are the dimensions of the prism? _______ by _______ by _______

6. How can Mandy's dad stack the boxes so he has enough stickers?

Name ______________________________

Use Reasoning (continued)

Answer 7 to **look back** at how you solved the problem?

7. **Reasoning** How did objects help you solve the problem.

Solve each problem. Use objects and reasoning.

8. Mandy's dad stacks 36 boxes, in a 3 by 3 by 4 rectangular prism, for shipping. All the boxes are the same size cube. He put a sticker on each side of a box that is on the outside when they are stacked. How many of the small boxes have stickers on 3 sides? On 2 sides? On 1 side? On no sides?

_______ on 3 sides _______ on 2 sides

_______ on 1 side _______ on no sides

9. David wants to make a flower garden by enclosing it with landscape timbers. If a landscape timber is 8 feet long, and he has 6 timbers, what is the maximum area of garden space he can enclose?

____

10. How can you cut a double-layer cake into 8 pieces with only 3 straight cuts? Hint: Use two pieces of paper to represent the two layers of the cake.

11. Mr. Lange cut a 25-foot rope into 12 equal-sized pieces. How many cuts did he make?

Name ______________________________

Draw a Picture

Braxton is making a diagram of the distance between his house and his grandmother's house. He lives 0.9 mile from his grandmother. He knows the store is 0.2 miles from his house and has it marked on the diagram below. Where should Braxton's grandmother's house be placed on the diagram?

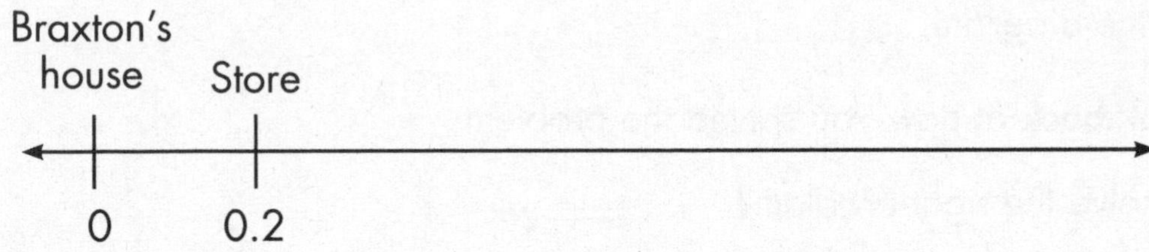

Solve by answering 1 to 6.

Answer 1 and 2 to **understand** the problem.

1. What do you know from reading the problem?

Braxton lives _______ mile from his grandmother.

The store is _______ mile from Braxton's house.

2. What do you need to find?

Answer 3 to 5 to **plan and solve** the problem.

You can solve by drawing a picture.

3. Mark the distance from 0 to 0.2 on a piece of paper. Then, use the marks to mark the distance 0.2 mile more from Braxton's house on the diagram. How far is this from Braxton's house? _______________

Name ______________________________

Draw a Picture (continued)

4. Mark and label this distance two more times.

5. Half of the distance between Braxton's house and the store is 0.1 mile. Mark 0.1 mile from Braxton's house on the diagram above. Use the distance from 0 to 0.1 to finish marking the distance to Grandmother's house in the diagram.

Answer 6 to **look back** at how you solved the problem.

6. Did you solve the right problem? ________

Solve each problem.

7. Alicia is making a diagram of the distance between her house and school. She lives 0.9 mile from school. She knows the park is 0.6 miles from her house and has it marked on the diagram below. Where should Alicia's school be placed on the diagram?

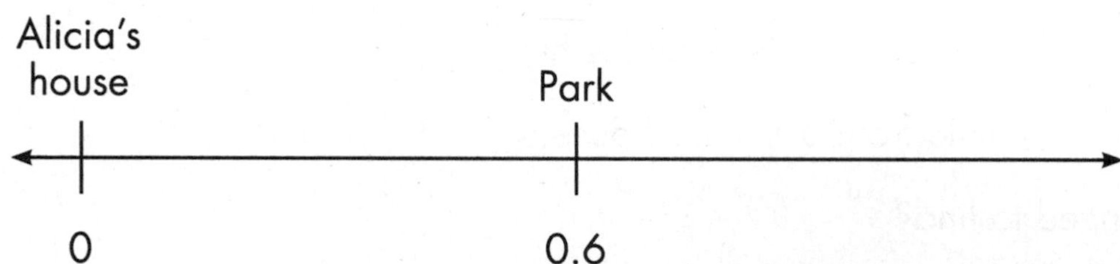

8. A helicopter is 150 feet above sea level. A submarine is directly below it, 100 feet below sea level. What is the distance between the helicopter and the submarine? ________

9. You are planting pepper plants in a garden. Your garden is only 48 inches long. The plants must be planted 6 inches apart and the first and last plant must be 6 inches from the edge of the garden. How many plants can you plant in a row?

____

10. You are in a town with square blocks. You walk 5 blocks east, 3 blocks north, then 2 blocks west. How many blocks do you need to walk to get back to your starting point?

____

Name ___________________________________

Draw a Picture

Katie has only white and blue socks. The ratio of white socks to blue socks is 5 to 6. What fraction of Katie's socks are blue?

Solve by answering 1 to 5.

Answer 1 and 2 to **understand** the problem.

1. What do you know from reading the problem?

Katie has only __________ and __________ socks.

The ratio of Katie's white socks to her blue socks is __________.

2. What do you need to find?

____

Answer 3 and 4 to **plan and solve** the problem.

You can solve by drawing a picture.

3. Draw a picture of Katie's socks so the ratio of white socks to blue socks is 5 to 6.

4. What fraction of Katie's socks are blue? _______

Answer 5 to **look back at and extend** the problem.

5. **Reasoning** How did a picture help you solve the problem?

6. If the ratio of white socks to blue socks was 8 to 10, what fraction of Katie's socks would be blue? Write the fraction in simplest form.

____

Name ____

Draw a Picture (continued)

Solve each problem by drawing or completing the picture provided.

7. At lunch, Sara and Jim are third and fourth in line. There are 7 people behind them. How many people are in line?

8. A roller coaster has a train of 5 cars that are each 6 feet long. The cars are 2 feet apart. How long is the train?

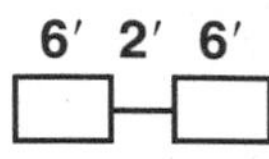

The train is _______ feet long.

9. A square garden is 10 feet long. A square walkway 3 feet wide goes all the way around the garden. How many feet of fence is needed to go around the walkway?

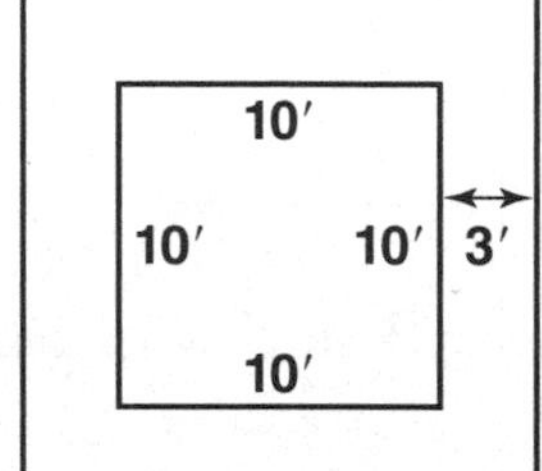

_______ feet of fence is needed.

10. Two-thirds of the area of a farm is planted with wheat. The wheat covers 4 acres. What is the area of the farm?

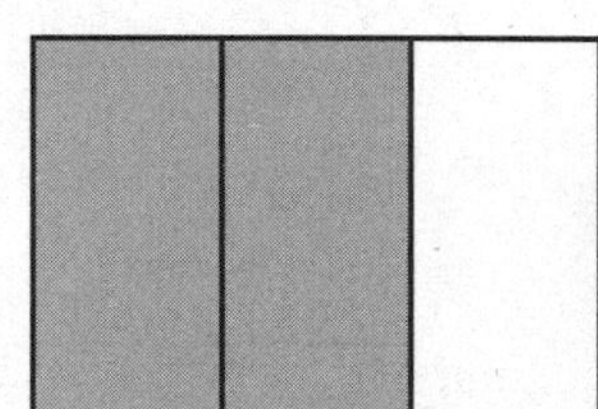

11. A straight fence is 24 feet long. There is a fence post every 6 feet. How many posts are there in the fence?

12. When a ball bounces, it returns to $\frac{1}{2}$ of its previous height. If Ken drops a ball from 20 feet, how many feet will it have traveled when it hits the ground the second time?

Name ______________________________

Intervention Lesson **J27**

Work Backward

Between 4:00 P.M. and 5:00 P.M., the temperature dropped 4 degrees. Every hour after that, the temperature dropped 2 degrees. At 8:00 P.M., the temperature was 52°F. What was the temperature at 4:00 P.M.?

F
70
60
50
40

8:00 P.M.

Solve by answering 1 to 7.

Answer 1 and 2 to **understand** the problem.

1. What do you know from reading the problem?

The temperature dropped _____ degrees, between 4:00 P.M. and 5:00 P.M.

The temperature dropped _____ degrees, every hour after 5:00 P.M.

The temperature was _____, at 8:00 P.M.

2. What do you need to find?

____

Answer 3 to 5 to **plan and solve** the problem.

You can solve by working backward.

3. The temperature dropped 2 degrees from 7:00 P.M. to 8:00 P.M. The temperature was 52°F at 8:00 p.m. What was the temperature at 7:00 P.M.? Write your answer in the diagram below.

4:00 P.M.	5:00 P.M.	6:00 P.M.	7:00 P.M.	8:00 P.M.

−4 → −2 → −2 → −2 →

				52°F

← +4 ← +2 ← +2 ← +2

Name ____________________

Work Backward (continued)

4. Find the temperature at 6:00 P.M., then 5:00 P.M., then 4:00 P.M. Write each in the diagram on the previous page.

5. What was the temperature at 4:00 P.M.? ______

Answer 6 and 7 to **look back and check** your solution to the problem.

6. The temperature dropped 2 degrees from 7:00 P.M. to 8:00 P.M., which means you subtract 2. When working backward from 8:00 P.M. to 7:00 P.M., do you add or subtract 2? ______

7. If the temperature was the one you found at 4:00 P.M. and changed as described in the problem, would it be 52°F at 8:00 P.M.? ______

Solve each problem.

8. It takes Josh 10 minutes to get ready for soccer practice and 25 minutes to bike to the field. He needs to eat a snack before he gets ready and that takes 15 minutes. Soccer practice is at 4:30. What time does Josh need to start eating his snack to get to soccer practice on time? ______

9. Lola took 45 minutes to get ready for school. She walked to school in 20 minutes and then waited 5 minutes before the bell rang at 8:55 A.M. What time did she get out of bed that morning?

______

10. The trip from your home to the museum takes 45 minutes. You need 1 hour and 30 minutes to tour a special exhibit in the museum. You want to finish the tour before 3:00 P.M. What is the latest time you should leave home to go to the museum?

______

Name ______________________________

Work Backward

Jean cuts 30 inches off a board to make a shelf. Then she cuts the rest of the board into 4 equal pieces. Each piece is 6 inches long. How long was the original board?

Solve by answering 1 to 5.

Answer 1 and 2 to **understand** the problem.

1. What do you know from reading the problem?

Jean cuts _____ inches off a board to make a shelf.

Then, Jean cuts the board into _____ equal pieces.

Each of the equal pieces is _____ inches long.

2. What do you need to find?

____

Answer 3 and 4 to **plan and solve** the problem.

You can solve by working backward.

3. Jean cut the board into 4 equal pieces and each piece was 6 inches long. How long was the board before Jean cut it into 4 equal parts? Write your answer in the diagram below.

Original board		
−30 →		÷ 4 →
		6
← +30		← ×4

4. How long was the board before Jean cut off 30 inches, that is, how long was the original board? _____

Name ______________________________

Work Backward (continued)

Answer 5 to **look back at and extend** the problem.

5. **Reasoning** Jean cut off 30 inches, which means she subtracted 30 inches from the length of the board. When working backward, do you add or subtract 30? ________

Solve each problem by working backward.

6. Jeb bought a CD for $14.99 plus $1.19 for tax. He had $3.82 left. How much money did he have before he bought the CD? ________

7. There were 7 people on a bus. At the next stop, 4 women got on and 4 men got off the bus. Of the 7 people on the bus, $\frac{4}{7}$ were women. How many women were on the bus to start? ________

8. A store reduced the price of a DVD player by $15. A week later, all prices in the store were cut in half for a clearance sale. The clearance price of the DVD player was $47. What was the original price? ________

9. Ana spent half her savings on a pair of skates. Then she spent $12 on a CD. If she earned $5 and now has $65, how much money did she have before she bought the skates? ________

Solve each problem. Use any strategy.

10. Charlotte bowled 3 games. Her average score was 142. What was her total for the 3 games together?

average score = total score ÷ number of games

____

11. Two families went bowling. They paid for 4 adult games and 4 bumper bowling games, but no one rented shoes. What was the total cost they paid?

Bowling Prices (per game)	
Adults	$3.35
Bumper bowling	$3.70
Shoe rental (per person)	$2.00

Name ____________________

Intervention Lesson **J29**

Make a Graph

Materials crayons or markers, grid paper

Students in two classes voted on the type of booth they would like to sponsor at the carnival. The results are in the tally charts below. Answer 1 to 4 to find which type of booth the two classes should sponsor together.

Mrs. Bentley's Class

Carnival Booth	Tally
Balloon Pop	~~IIII~~ IIII
Ring Toss	~~IIII~~ III
Face Painting	IIII

Mr. Chavez's Class

Carnival Booth	Tally
Balloon Pop	~~IIII~~
Ring Toss	~~IIII~~ III
Face Painting	~~IIII~~ III

1. Draw a bar graph of each set of data.

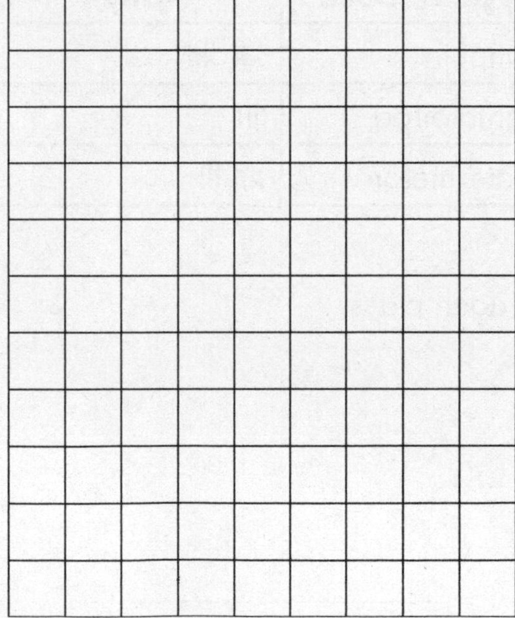

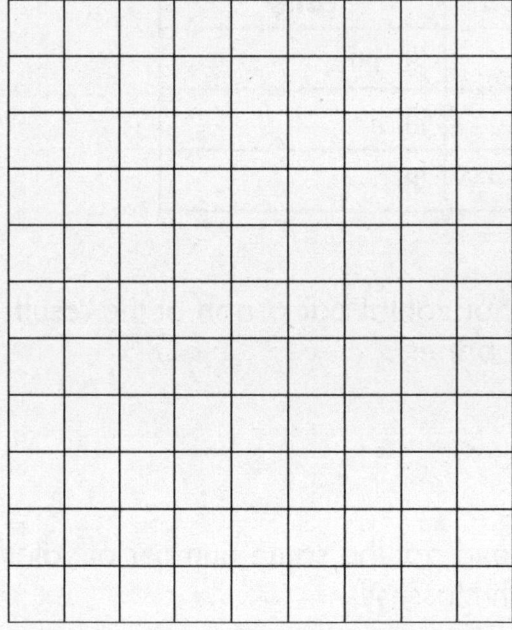

Name ______________________________

Make a Graph (continued)

2. What was the least favorite type of booth of the students in Mrs. Bentley's Class? __________

3. What was the least favorite type of booth of the students in Mr. Chavez's Class? __________

4. **Reasoning** Which type of booth should the two classes sponsor together? Explain your choice.

Two classes voted on which type of seed they would like to plant in their garden. The results are shown in the tally charts below. Use the information in the tally charts for 5-8.

Ms. Aydin's Class

Type of Seed	Tally
Pumpkin	𝍸 𝍸
Cantaloupe	𝍸 II
Watermelon	𝍸

Mr. Brown's Class

Type of Seed	Tally
Pumpkin	𝍸 𝍸
Cantaloupe	IIII
Watermelon	𝍸 III

5. Draw a horizontal bar graph of the results for each class. Use grid paper.

6. Which seed got the same number of votes from both classes? __________

7. Cantaloupe got more votes from which class?

8. **Reasoning** Was the favorite seed the same for both classes? Explain how you can tell from the graphs.

Name ______________________________

Intervention Lesson **J30**

Make a Graph

Will's family has two dogs. The tables below show how each of the two dogs grew as puppies in their first 5 months. How does the growth of the two puppies compare?

Socks' Growth	
Month	**Weight (pounds)**
1	2
2	5
3	10
4	8
5	15

Buddy's Growth	
Month	**Weight (pounds)**
1	2
2	6
3	9
4	15
5	20

You can solve by making and interpreting two line graphs. Answer 1 to 6.

1. Make a line graph of each set of data.

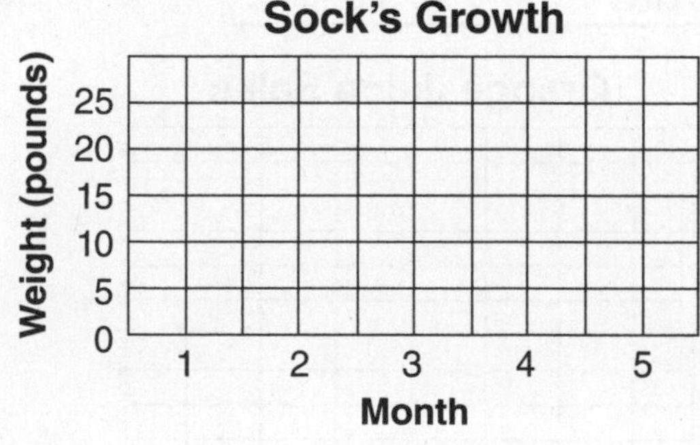

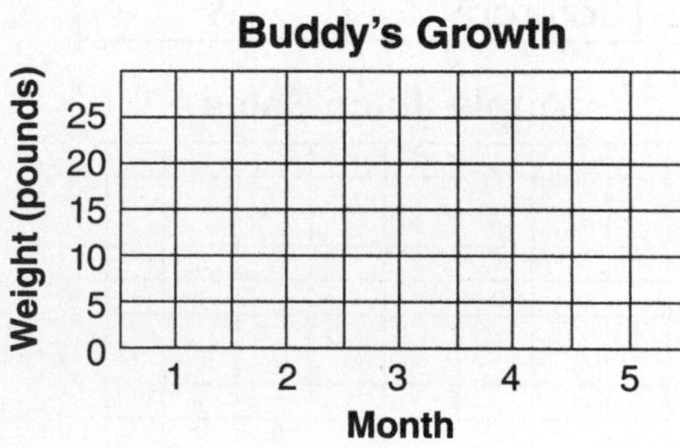

2. Which puppy had the most steady weight gain? ____________

3. Which puppy had the greatest weight gain in one month? ____________

4. Which puppy lost weight one month? ____________

5. **Reasoning** Which full grown dog probably weighs the most? Why?

Name ______________________________

Make a Graph (continued)

Answer 6 to **look back at and extend** the problem.

6. **Reasoning** How did the line graphs help you compare the growth of the two puppies?

7. The data in the two tables below show the gallons of apple and orange juice sold by a company each day for a week. Make a bar graph of each set of data.

Apple Juice Sales	
Day	**Gallons**
Sunday	4
Monday	8
Tuesday	10
Wednesday	14
Thursday	18
Friday	7
Saturday	9

Orange Juice Sales	
Day	**Gallons**
Sunday	6
Monday	8
Tuesday	10
Wednesday	12
Thursday	14
Friday	16
Saturday	18

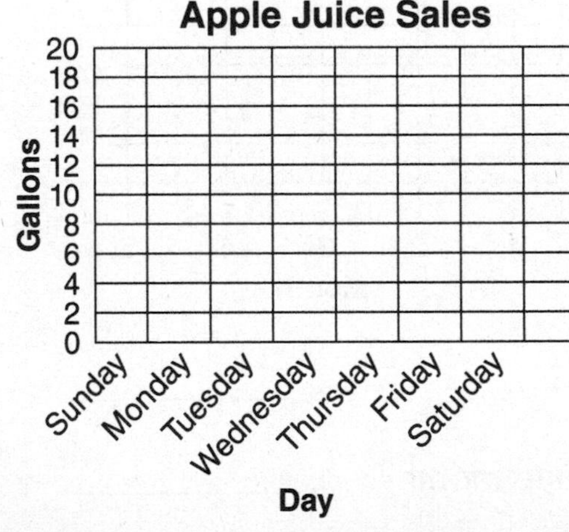

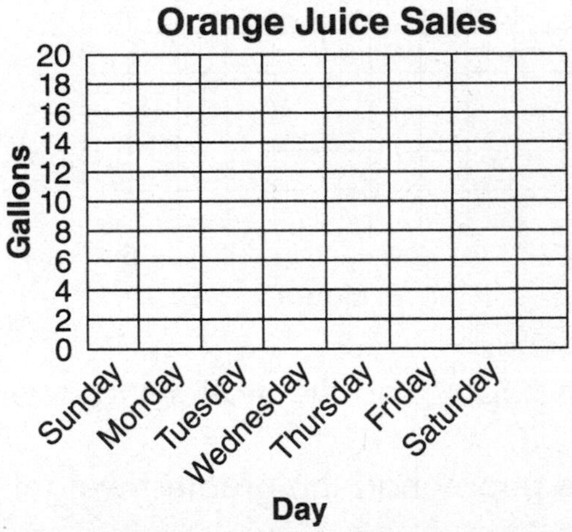

Use the bar graphs above for Exercises 8 to 10.

8. Which type of juice had a steady increase in sales? ______________

9. Between which two days did the sales of apple juice decrease? ______________

10. On which two days did the company sell a lot more orange juice than apple juice? ______________

Name ______________________________

Intervention Lesson **J31**

Analyze Relationships

Materials cubes, 20 for each student or pair

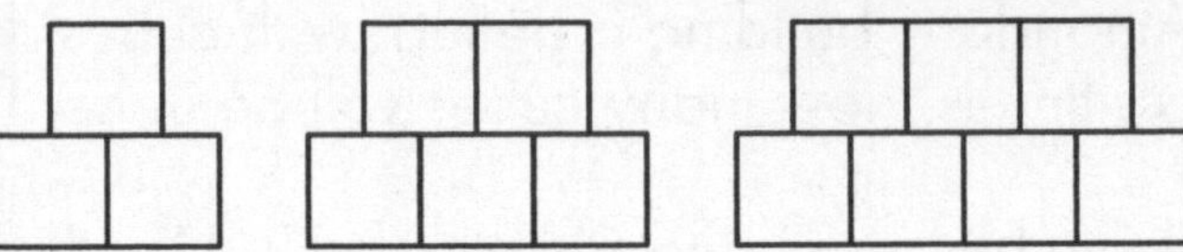

Bob is building a brick wall. He is using a growing pattern as shown to the right. If the pattern continues, how many bricks will be in the sixth design?

Solve by answering 1 to 6.

Answer 1 and 2 to **understand** the problem.

1. What do you know from looking at the diagram?

The first three designs have _____, _____, and _____ bricks.

2. What do you need to find?

Answer 3 to 5 to **plan and solve** the problem.

You can solve the problem by finding a pattern.

3. Use cubes to create each design, in order. How many more cubes do you need to use for each new design?

4. Continue the pattern. Use cubes if you like.

3, 5, 7, _____, _____, _____

5. How many bricks are in the sixth design?

Answer 6 through 8 to **look back** at how you solved the problem.

6. **Reasoning** What was the pattern?

7. How many bricks will be in the tenth design?

8. If each cube represents 1 cubic unit, what is the volume of the sixth design?

Name ______________________________

Analyze Relationships (continued)

Amanda is building a pattern with cubes. If the pattern continues, how many cubes will be in her fourth design?

Solve by answering 9 through 13. Use the diagram to the right.

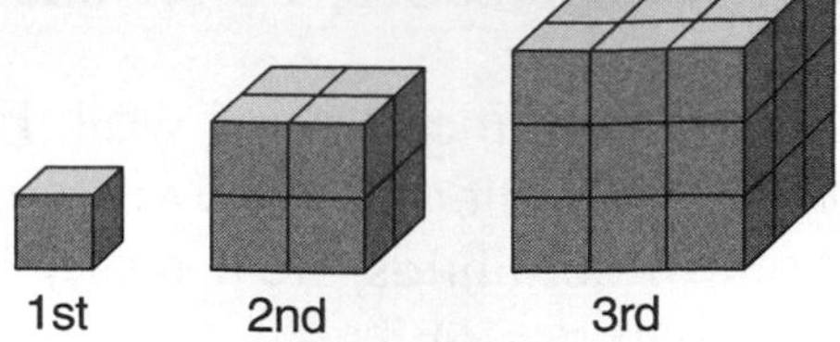

9. How many layers are in the third design?

10. How many cubes are in each layer of the third design?

11. How many layers will be in the fourth design?

12. How many cubes will be in each layer of the fourth design?

13. How many cubes will be in the fourth design?

Answer 14 as an extension to Exercises 9 through 13. Use the diagram above to help.

14. If each cube has a volume of 1 cubic centimeter, what is the volume of each of the 3 designs shown in the pattern?

Use cubes to answer 15.

15. **Reasoning** One rectangular prism has 4 cubes in each of 3 layers. Another rectangular prism has 3 cubes in each of 4 layers. Which rectangular prism has the greater volume?

Name ______________________________

Make and Test Generalizations

Intervention Lesson **J32**

How are the polygons alike?

Polygon 1 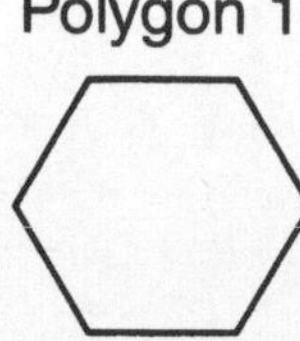

Polygon 2 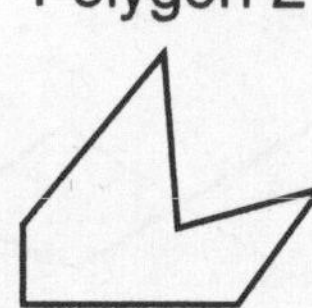

Polygon 3 

Solve by answering 1 to 5.

1. Complete the generalization about the polygons.

All the polygons have _____ sides.

2. Test the generalization.

Does Polygon 1 have 6 sides? _____ Polygon 2? _____

Polygon 3? _____

Since the generalization holds for all 3 polygons, it is true.

3. Test the following generalization: All the sides of each polygon are the same length.

Are all the sides of Polygon 1 the same length? _____

Are all the sides of Polygon 2 the same length? _____

Are all the sides of Polygon 3 the same length? _____

4. Is the conjecture true? _____

5. **Reasoning** Is the following generalization true? All the polygons have at least one obtuse angle. Explain.

Name ___________________________

Make and Test Generalizations (continued)

Make a generalization about each set of figures. Test your generalization. If the generalization is not true, make another generalization until you find one that is true.

6. 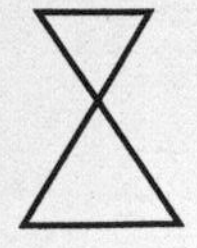  

7. N F A Z Y

8. 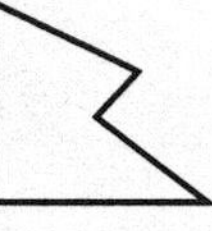 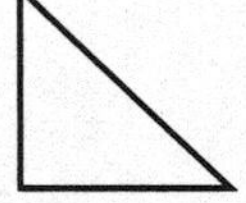 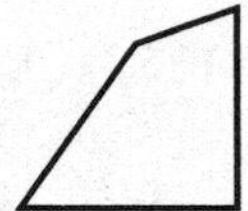

9.   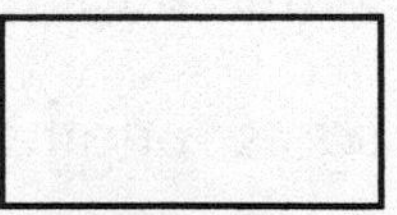

10. 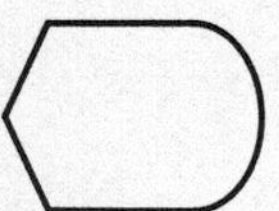 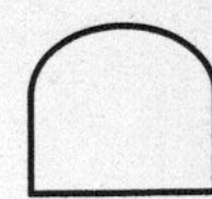 

Name ______________________________

Intervention Lesson **J33**

Make and Test Conjectures

If a number *n* is a factor of a number *m*, what is true about the factors of *n* and *m*?

Solve by answering 1 to 5.

Start by looking at some examples and making a conjecture.

1. The table below has some examples for *m* and *n*. Notice each value of *n* is a factor of the value of *m* in the same row. Complete the table.

m	Factors of *m*	*n*	Factors of *n*
12	1, 2, 3, 4, 6, 12	6	1, 2, 3, 6
28		14	
24		12	
36		12	
36		18	

2. Complete the conjecture.

If a number *n* is a factor of a number *m*, then all the factors of

_______ are factors _______.

A **counterexample**, is an example which proves a conjecture is not true.

3. Try to find a counterexample for your conjecture. List the numbers you try.

_______ and _______ _______ and _______ _______ and _______

4. Could you find a counterexample? _______

A counterexample can prove a conjecture is false, but it cannot prove that a conjecture is true.

5. Is your conjecture proven false? _______ Is it proven true? _______

Name ______________________________

Make and Test Conjectures (continued)

Make and test a conjecture about the factors of *n* and twice *n* by answering 6 to 9.

6. Complete the table. Look for a pattern.

n	Number of Factors of *n*	2*n*	Number of Factors of 2*n*
6	4	12	6
14		28	
12		24	
40		80	

7. Complete the conjecture.

The number that is twice *n* has ______ more factors than *n*.

8. Try to find a counterexample for your conjecture. Either give the counterexample or list at least 3 sets of numbers you try.

9. Is your conjecture proven false? ______ Is it proven true? ______

Write a conjecture to answer each question.

10. How are the patterns alike?

Benita's pattern is: 2, 4, 6, 8, 10, 12, 14, ...

Carol's pattern is: 1, 3, 5, 7, 9, 11, 13, ...

11. How did Beth sort the shapes into Groups A and B?

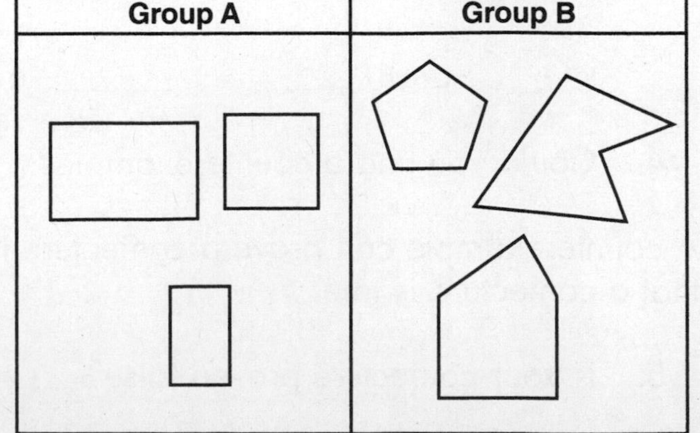

12. Make another conjecture about how Beth sort the shapes.

Name ______________________________

Intervention Lesson **J34**

Reasonableness

A container when empty weighs 150 pounds. If the container is filled with 312 pounds, what is the total weight of the container and its contents?

Solve by answering 1 to 7.

Answer 1 and 2 to **understand** the problem.

1. What do you know from reading the problem?

The empty container weighs _______ pounds.

The contents of the container weighs _______ pounds.

2. What do you need to find?

Answer 3 and 4 to **plan and solve** the problem.

3. How can you solve the problem? ______________________

4. What is the total weight of the container and its contents? _______ pounds

Answer 5 to 7 to **check** that your answer is reasonable.

5. Estimate 150 + 312 by rounding to the nearest hundred.

150 + 312 is about _______

6. Is your answer to the problem close to the estimate? _______

Since the answer of 462 is close to the estimate of 500, the answer 462 pounds is **reasonable**.

7. Did you answer the right question? _______

Name ___________________________

Intervention Lesson **J34**

Reasonableness (continued)

Solve each problem. Then explain why your answer is reasonable.

8. Karen had some stickers. She gave 34 butterfly stickers and 27 flag stickers to Bill. How many stickers did Karen give to Bill?

9. Harold collects stamps. He has 32 stamps from the United States and 18 stamps from other countries. How many more United States stamps does Harold have than international stamps?

10. Some students took a survey about cats and dogs. They found that 87 students like dogs and 56 students like cats. How many students voted for cats or dogs?

11. On Friday, 214 people came to the concert. On Saturday, 298 people came. How many people came on both nights combined?

12. At TV City, a new television costs $629. At Discount Place, the same TV costs $498. How much more does the TV cost at TV City than at Discount Place?

Name ______________________________

Reasonableness

Ahmed has 183 postcards in his collection. He mounts them on sheets of poster board, with 12 postcards on each board. How many sheets of poster board does he need to mount all of his postcards?

Solve by answering 1 to 7.

Answer 1 and 2 to **understand** the problem.

1. What do you know from reading the problem?

Ahmed has ______ postcards.

Ahmed puts ______ postcards on each sheet of poster board.

2. What do you need to find?

Answer 3 and 4 to **plan and solve** the problem.

You can solve by drawing a picture.

3. How can you solve the problem? ______________________________

4. How many sheets of poster board does Ahmed need to mount all of his postcards? ______.

Answer 5 to 7 to **check** that your answer is reasonable.

5. Did you answer the right question? Explain.

6. Estimate 183 ÷ 12. 183 ÷ 12 is between ______ and ______.

Name ____

Reasonableness (continued)

7. Is your answer between the numbers in the estimate? _______

Since the answer of 16 is between 10 and 20, the answer 16 is **reasonable**.

Solve each problem. Then explain why your answer is reasonable.

8. A swimming pool is 11 meters wide and 38 meters long. What is the area of the swimming pool?

9. The 272 students at Crestwood School are going on a field trip to the art museum. If the students travel in 6 buses, how many students are on each bus?

10. For lunch, Jason bought a chicken sandwich for $3.25, a carton of milk for $1.10, and a cookie for $0.50. How much did he spend?

11. Tina has a board 16 feet long. She is going to cut as many 3-foot shelves from the board as she can. How much of the board will she have left?

12. Mr. Rohrs knows that it takes 7 bricks to cover 1 square foot of surface area. How many bricks will he need to construct the wall shown?

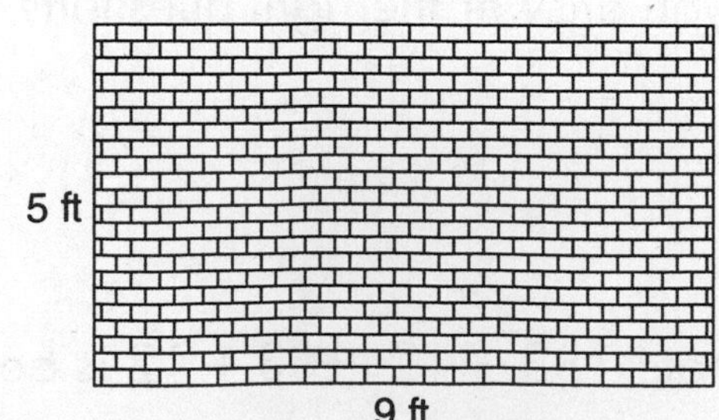

Name ____________________

Intervention Lesson **J36**

Use Representations

Eric walked to Kim's house to return a book that he had borrowed. Eric stayed at Kim's house for a few minutes and then walked home.

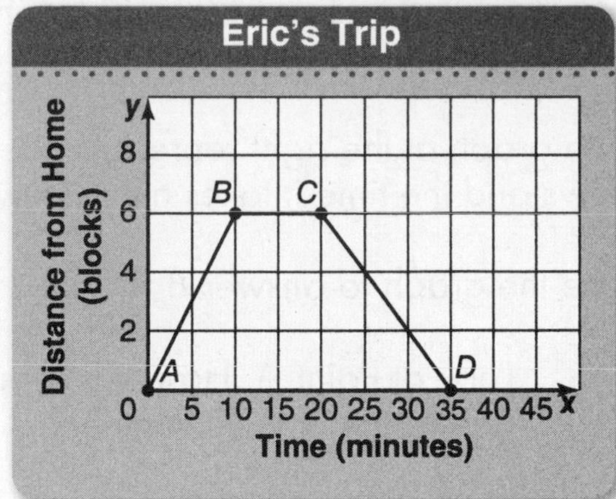

The graph at the right represents the distance Eric walked and how long it took Eric to walk to Kim's house and then back home.

Use the graph to answer 1 to 7.

1. Eric left home at Point *A* and arrived at Kim's house at Point *B*. How long did it take Eric to walk to Kim's house?

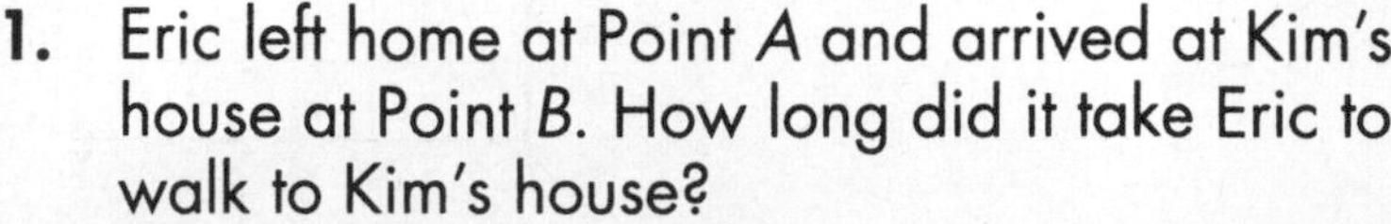

____

2. How far is Kim's house from Eric's house?

____

3. Which part of the graph represents the time that Eric was at Kim's house?

____

4. Which part of the graph represents the time it took Eric to walk home?

____

5. Did Eric walk faster to Kim's house or back home to his own house? Explain.

6. The ordered pair (10, 6) locates Point *B* on the graph. What ordered pair locates Point *C* on the graph?

____

7. What do the coordinates (35, 0) represent?

Name ______________________________

Use Representations (continued)

Sarah is sewing buttons on shirts. She began sewing at 10:30 A.M.

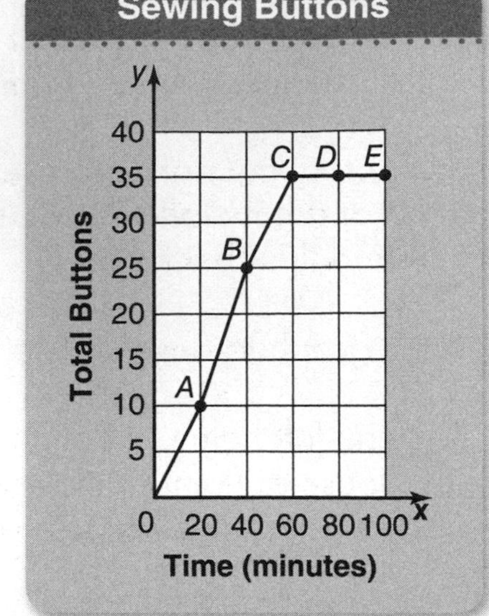

The graph at the right represents the number of buttons Sarah sews and the time it takes her to sew them on the shirts.

Use the graph to answer 8 to 13.

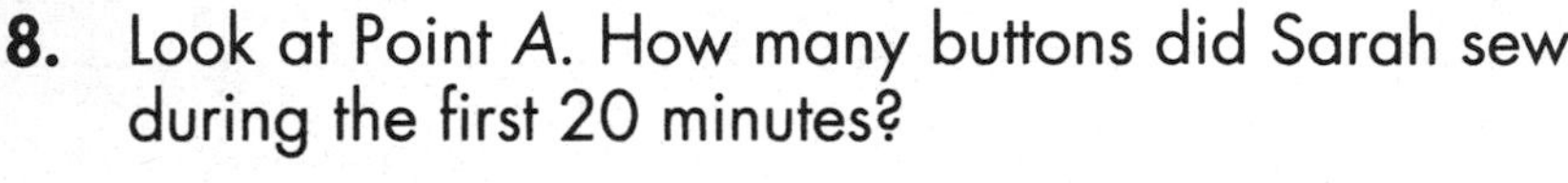

8. Look at Point *A*. How many buttons did Sarah sew during the first 20 minutes?

____

9. What ordered pair locates Point *B* on the graph?

____

10. How many buttons did Sarah sew in all?

____

11. Did Sarah sew more buttons in the period of time between Points *A* and *B* or in the period of time between Points *B* and *C*? Explain.

12. What might have happened between Points *C* and *E*?

13. Write another story to fit the data on the graph.

Name ____________________

Intervention Lesson **J37**

Writing to Explain

Materials crayons or markers

At Sam's Sandwich Shop, Toni ate $\frac{3}{4}$ of a medium sandwich, Becky ate $\frac{3}{4}$ of a small sandwich, and Mary Jo ate $\frac{6}{8}$ of a medium sandwich. Explain why Toni and Mary Jo ate the same amount of sandwich, but Toni and Becky ate different amounts.

Solve by answering 1 to 8.

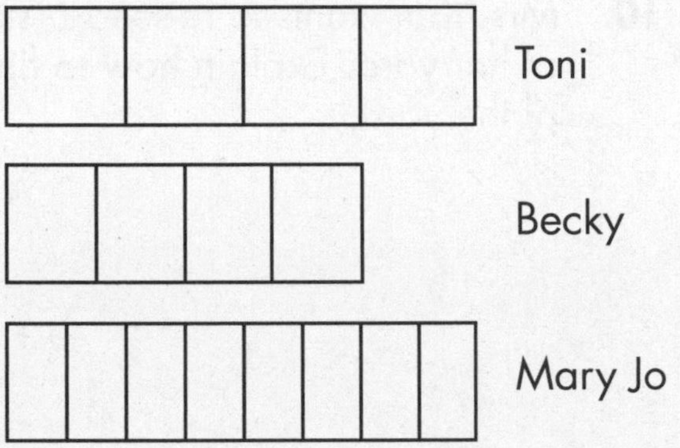

Toni

Becky

Mary Jo

1. Toni ate ______ of a medium sandwich. Color the diagram at the right to show what Toni ate.

2. Becky ate ______ of a small sandwich.

3. How did the size of Becky's sandwich compare to the size of Toni's sandwich?

4. Color the diagram above to show what Becky ate.

5. Mary Jo ate ______ of a medium sandwich.

6. How did the size of May Jo's sandwich compare to the size of Toni's sandwich?

7. Color the diagram above to show what Mary Jo ate.

8. Use the diagram to explain why Toni and Mary Jo ate the same amount, but Toni and Becky ate different amounts.

Name ____

Writing to Explain (continued)

Write to explain.

9. Explain how you find the perimeter of the figure shown on the right.

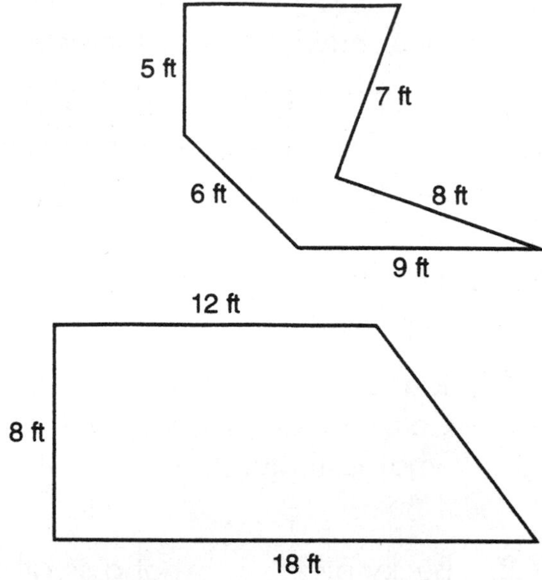

10. Mrs. Kim wants to re-seed a small section of her yard. Explain how to find the area of the yard.

Solve the problem. Write to explain how you solved.

11. The Oak Street Theater has 4 sections of seating. Each section has 5 rows of seats. Two sections have 4 seats in each row. The other sections have 3 seats in each row. How many seats are there in the theater?

Name ______________________________

Writing to Explain

Materials crayons, markers, or colored pencils

A student's work is shown at the right. Is the answer correct? Draw a picture to explain why or why not.

Max's Media gives six DVD rentals for the price of 5. If Ann Maria pays for 15 rentals, how many rentals does she get in all?

15 − 5 = 10
6 + 10 = 16
She gets 16 rentals.

Solve by answering 1 and 2.

1. Color the counters below to represent the DVDs paid for in one color and the free ones in another color.

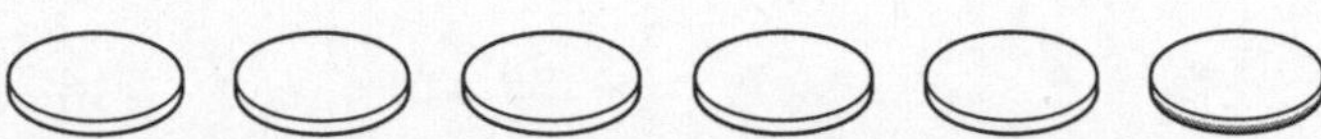

2. Repeat the set of counters until there are 15 DVDs paid for.

If Anna Maria pays for 15 rentals, how many rentals does she get in all?

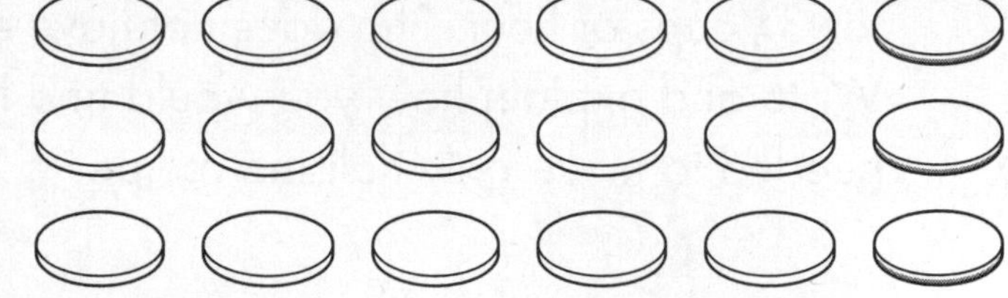

She gets ______ rentals in all.

The student's answer is not correct.

3. Fill in the blanks to explain how to write and solve a proportion to solve the problem.

Let r be the ______________________ Anna Maria gets.

Then $\frac{5}{6} = \frac{\square}{r}$.

Using cross products, $5r =$ ______.

$r =$ ______

Anna Maria gets ______ rentals in all.

Name ______________________________________

Writing to Explain (continued)

Explain your solution to each problem. Show your work.

4. Manuel went on a 400-mile trip with his friend Julio. If Manuel drove $\frac{3}{5}$ of the trip, how far did he drive?

5. Sliced turkey cost $2.89 per pound. Sliced beef costs $3.11 per pound. Majorie buys 2 pounds of turkey and 1 pound of beef. If she pays for the meat with a $10 bill, will she get change? Explain how you made your estimate.

6. Mrs. Barker is making chocolate chip cookies. Her recipe calls for $3\frac{1}{2}$ cups of flour. She does not have enought flour for a full recipe. Write and explain how you would find how many cups of flour are needed to make only half the recipe.

7. How many square feet of roofing paper does Joe need in order to put a new roof on his dog house? The roof has 2 rectangular sides, and each side of the roof measures 3 feet by $2\frac{1}{2}$ feet.

Name ____________________

Intervention Lesson **J39**

Make and Test Generalizations

Use the set of shapes to the right to answer 1 through 3.

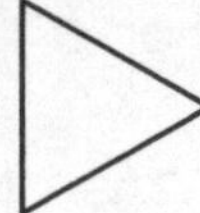

Jill is making 3 sandboxes using the shapes shown to the right. Her friend Beth comes over to help. Jill does not show Beth the shapes but makes a generalization about them.

1. What shape is each of the three shapes shown? What do you know about these shapes?

2. What are some generalizations that Jill could have made about the three shapes?

3. How can you test each generalization?

For 4 and 5, make and test a generalization for each set of shapes.

4.

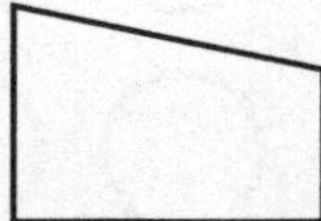

____

Test: ____________________

5.

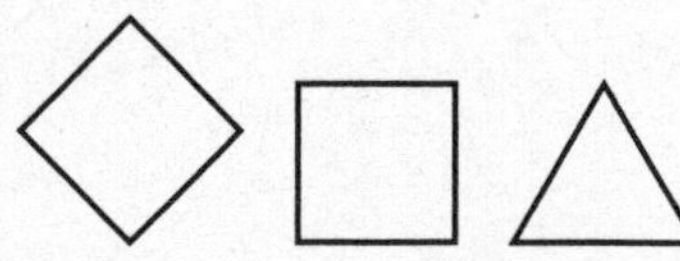

____

Test: ____________________

Name ______________________________

Make and Test Generalizations (continued)

For 6 through 9, make and test a generalization.

6. How are the numbers 15, 25, 35, and 45 alike? Make and test a generalization.

7. Review each product and its factors in the following multiplication sentences:

$7 \times 6 = 42$ $4 \times 6 = 24$ $7 \times 9 = 63$

Make and test a generalization about factors and products for whole numbers.

8. Bo has 3 arrays of counters as shown below.

Make and test a generalization about the 3 arrays.

9. **Reasoning** Alex says that the sum of an even and odd number is even. Is this generalization true? If not, explain why not.

Name ______________________________

Make and Test Conjectures

A **conjecture** is a generalization that you think is true.

For 1 through 3, make a conjecture and test it. If your conjecture is not correct, then use reasoning to make another conjecture.

1. What type of sum do you get when you add two odd numbers?

Conjecture 1: ______________________________

Test: ______________________________

Conjecture 2: ______________________________

Test: ______________________________

2. What type of quotient do you get when you divide an even number by an odd number?

Conjecture 1: ______________________________

Test: ______________________________

Conjecture 2: ______________________________

Test: ______________________________

3. What type of product do you get when both factors are odd?

Conjecture 1: ______________________________

Test: ______________________________

Conjecture 2: ______________________________

Test: ______________________________

Name ______________________________

Make and Test Conjectures (continued)

For 4 through 6, test the conjecture and tell whether it is true. If it is not true, provide an explanation.

4. The number 24 has 6 factors.

Test: ______________________________

Explanation: ______________________________

5. The only equivalent fractions for $\frac{1}{2}$ are $\frac{2}{4}$ and $\frac{3}{6}$.

Test: ______________________________

____

Explanation: ______________________________

____

6. All quadrilaterals are parallelograms.

Test: ______________________________

____

Explanation: ______________________________

____

7. Write and test a conjecture about squares and rectangles.

Conjecture: ______________________________

Test: ______________________________

____

____